Brickwork

NVQ and Technical Certificate **Level 3**

www.harcourt.co.uk

✓ Free online support
✓ Useful weblinks
✓ 24 hour online ordering

01865 888118

Heinemann

Heinemann is an imprint of Harcourt Education Limited, a company incorporated in England and Wales, having its registered office: Halley Court, Jordan Hill, Oxford OX2 8EJ. Registered company number: 3099304

www.harcourt.co.uk

Heinemann is the registered trademark of Harcourt Education Limited

First published 2007

12 11 10 09 08 07
10 9 8 7 6 5 4 3 2 1

British Library Cataloguing in Publication Data is available from the British Library on request.

ISBN 978 0 435464 75 2

Copyright notice

Designed and typeset by HL Studios
Produced by HL Studios

Illustrated by HL Studios

Cover design by GD Associates

Printed in the UK by Scotprint

...e been prepared according to the standards reasonably ...levant subject matter. However, you should be aware ...at different employers may adopt different standards ...ng any practical activity, you should always carry out you ...uiries and investigations into appropriate standards and

Contents

Acknowledgements

The author and publisher would like to thank the following individuals and organisations for permission to reproduce photographs:

Alamy / Adrian Sherratt pp 55, 91, 141, 147, 161; Alamy / Justin Kase p7; Alamy / Mark Boulton p119; Alamy / Niall McDiarmid p111 (left); Alamy / Nic Hamilton p3; Alamy / Nikreates p86; Alamy / The Photolibrary Wales p14; Alamy / Tim Hurst p111 (right); Celcon pp69, 72, 74 (bottom), 75 (middle right), 77; Construction Photography / Chris Henderson p9; Construction Photography / CP Stock p43; Construction photography / Darren Holden p1; Construction Photography / DIY Photolibrary p40; Construction Photography / Grant Smith p12; Construction Photography / Paul McMullin p39; Construction Photography / Xavier de Canto p17; Corbis / Creasource p27; Corbis / Martin Meyer / Zefa p42; Harcourt Ltd / Ian Wedgewood p73, 74 (top three), 75 (top, middle left, bottom three), 79, 83, 84, 108, 110, 131; iStockPhoto.com / Marco Prandina p105; Photographers Direct / Anthony Hatley p100; Photographers Direct / Bjorn Beheydt p25; Photographers Direct / Dave Armstrong (bottom); Photographers Direct / David Griffiths p23; Photographers Direct / Jim Worlding p81, 82 (top); Photographers Direct / John Gaffen p88; Photographers Direct / Jonathan Howell p121; Photographers Direct / Kevin Lockhart p85; Photographers Direct / Robert Clare p151; Science Photo Library / Garry Watson p8 (left); Topham Picturepoint p8 (middle and right).

Every effort has been made to contact copyright holders of material reproduced in this book. Any omissions will be rectified in subsequent printings if notice is given to the publishers.

About this book

This book has been written based on a concept used within Carillion Training Centres for many years. That concept is about providing learners with the necessary information they need to support their studies and at the same time ensuring that it is presented in a style which they find both manageable and relevant.

The content of this book has been put together by a team of instructors, each of whom have a wealth of knowledge and experience in both training for NVQs and Technical Certificates and their trade.

This book has been produced to help the learner build a sound knowledge and understanding of all aspects of the NVQ and Technical Certificate requirements associated with their trade. It has also been designed to provide assistance when revising for Technical Certificate end tests and NVQ job knowledge tests.

Each chapter of this book relates closely to a particular unit of the NVQ or Technical Certificate and aims to provide just the right level of information needed to form the required knowledge and understanding of that subject area.

This book builds on the basic information provided by the Level 2 book, providing more specific terminology and in-depth information about the tools, materials and methods of work required to enable you to complete work activities effectively and productively. Upon completion of your studies, this book will remain a valuable source of information and support when carrying out your work activities.

For further information on how the content of this student book matches to the unit requirements of the NVQ and Intermediate Construction Award, please visit www.heinemann.co.uk and follow the FE and Vocational link, followed by the Construction link, where a detailed mapping document is available for download.

How this book can help you

You will discover a variety of features throughout this book, each of which have been designed and written to increase and improve your knowledge and understanding. These features are:

- Photographs – many photographs that appear in this book are specially taken and will help you to follow a step-by-step procedure or identify a tool or material.
- Illustrations – clear and colourful drawings will give you more information about a concept or procedure.
- Definitions – new or difficult words are picked out in bold in the text and defined in the margin.
- Remember – key concepts or facts are highlighted in these margin boxes.
- Find out – carry out these short activities and gain further information and understanding of a topic area.
- Did you know? – interesting facts about the building process
- Safety tips – follow the guidance in these margin boxes to help you work safely.
- FAQs – frequently asked questions appear in all chapters along with informative answers from the experts.
- On the job scenarios – read about a real-life situation and answer the questions at the end. what would you do? (Answers can be found in the Tutor Resource Disk that accompanies this book.)
- End of chapter knowledge checks – test your understanding and recall of a topic by completing these questions.
- Glossary – at the end of this book you will find a comprehensive glossary that defines all the bold words and phrases found in the text. A great quick reference tool.

chapter 1

Health and Safety

OVERVIEW

The construction industry is one of the most dangerous industries in the UK. Every year over 100 people are killed and thousands seriously injured, while thousands more suffer health problems such as **dermatitis**, **asbestosis** and deafness. You can see why learning as much as you can about health and safety is very important.

Level 2 gave a good grounding in health and safety and informed you of what you need to know and do. This book takes things a step further: as a Level 3 candidate working in a more supervisory role, your responsibilities and actions will be different.

This chapter will cover:

- health and safety legislation
- health and welfare
- risk assessments.

Health and safety legislation

Definition

Hazardous – dangerous or unsafe

While at work, whatever your location or type of work, you need to be aware that there is important **legislation** you must comply with. Health and safety legislation is there not just to protect you, but also states what you must and must not do to ensure that no workers are placed in a situation hazardous to themselves or others.

Each piece of legislation covers your own responsibilities as an employee and those of your employer – it is vital that you are aware of both. As a Level 3 candidate, you not only have to think of your responsibilities for your own actions, but must also consider your supervisory responsibilities for others. These may involve ensuring that others are aware of legislation and considering such legislation when you are overseeing others' work.

What is legislation?

Legislation means a law or set of laws passed by Parliament, often called an Act. There are hundreds of Acts covering all manner of work from hairdressing to construction. Each Act states the duties of the **employer** and **employee**. If an employer or employee does something they shouldn't – or doesn't do something they should – they can end up in court and be fined or even imprisoned.

Approved code of practice, guidance notes and safety policies

Definition

Proactive – acting in advance, before something happens (such as an accident)

Reactive – acting after something happens, in response to it

As well as Acts, there are two sorts of codes of practice and guidance notes: those produced by the **Health and Safety Executive (HSE)**, and those created by companies themselves. Most large construction companies – and many smaller ones – have their own guidance notes, which go further than health and safety law. For example, the law states that that everyone must wear safety boots in a hazardous area, but a company's code may state that everyone must wear safety boots at all times. This is called taking a **proactive** approach, rather than a **reactive** one.

Most companies have some form of **safety policy** outlining the company's commitment and stating what they plan to do to ensure that all work is carried out as safely as possible. As an employee, you should make sure you understand the company's safety policy as well as their codes of practice. If you act against company policy you may not be prosecuted in court, but you could still be disciplined by the company or even fired.

When you are acting as a supervisor you will need to ensure that staff you are supervising understand the safety policy too. The safety policy may even require you to take on further responsibilities as a supervisor, such as running safety drills and checks: if so you will need to understand what is involved in these and ask for any necessary support or training from your employer.

Health and safety legislation you need to be aware of

There are some 20 pieces of legislation you will need to be aware of, each of which sets out requirements for employers and often employees. One phrase often comes up here – '*so far as is reasonably practicable*'. This means that health and safety must be adhered to at all times, but must take a common sense, practical approach.

For example, the Health and Safety at Work Act 1974 states that an employer must *so far as is reasonably practicable* ensure that a safe place of work is provided. Yet employers are not expected to do everything they can to protect their staff from lightning strikes, as there is only a 1 in 800,000 chance of this occurring – this would not be reasonable!

We will now look at the regulations that will affect you most.

Legislation is there to protect employees and the public alike

The Health and Safety at Work Act (HASAW) 1974

HASAW applies to all types and places of work and to employers, employees, the self-employed, sub-contractors and even suppliers. The act is there to protect not only the people at work but also the general public, who may be affected in some way by the work that has been or will be carried out.

The main **objectives** of the health and safety at work act are to:

- ensure the health, safety and welfare of all persons at work
- protect the general public from all work activities
- control the use, handling, storage and transportation of explosives and highly flammable substances
- control the release of noxious or offensive substances into the atmosphere.

To ensure that these objectives are met there are duties for all employers, employees and suppliers.

Definition

Access – entrance, a way in

Egress – exit, a way out

PPE – personal protective equipment, such as gloves, a safety harness or goggles

Employer's duties

Employers must:

- provide safe **access** and **egress** to and within the work area
- provide a safe place to work
- provide and maintain plant and machinery that is safe and without risks to health
- provide information, instruction, training and supervision to ensure the health and safety at work of all employees
- ensure safety and the absence of risks to health in connection with the handling, storage and transportation of articles and substances
- have a written safety policy that must be revised and updated regularly, and ensure all employees are aware of it
- involve trade union safety representatives, where appointed, in all matters relating to health and safety
- provide and not charge for **personal protective equipment (PPE)**.

Definition

Omission – something that has not been done or has been missed out

Obligation – something you have a duty or a responsibility to do

Employee's duties

The employee must:

- take reasonable care for his/her own health and safety
- take reasonable care for the health and safety of anyone who may be affected by his/her acts or **omissions**
- co-operate with his/her employer or any other person to ensure legal **obligations** are met
- not misuse or interfere with anything provided for their health and safety
- use any equipment and safeguards provided by his/her employer.

Those supervising others will need to make sure that staff are using all safety equipment in the appropriate way, and are taking any necessary steps to ensure that they do not jeopardise their own or others' safety.

Employees cannot be charged for anything that has been done or provided for them to ensure that legal requirements on health and safety are met. The self-employed and sub-contractors have the same duties as employees – and if they have employees of their own, they must obey the duties set down for employers.

Supplier's duties

Persons designing, manufacturing, importing or supplying articles or substances for use at work must ensure that:

- articles are designed and constructed so that they will be safe and without risk to health at all times while they are being used or constructed
- substances will be safe and without risk to health at all times when being used, handled, transported and stored
- tests on articles and substances are carried out as necessary
- adequate information is provided about the use, handling, transporting and storing of articles or substances.

HASAW, like most of the other acts mentioned, is enforced by the Health and Safety Executive (HSE). HSE inspectors visit sites and have the power to:

- enter any premises at any reasonable time
- take a police constable with them
- examine and investigate anything on the premises
- take samples
- take possession of any dangerous article or substance
- issue improvement notices giving a company a certain amount of time to sort out a health and safety problem
- issue a **prohibition** notice stopping all work until the site is deemed safe
- **prosecute** people who break the law including employers, employees, self-employed, manufacturers and suppliers.

Provision and Use of Work Equipment Regulations 1998 (PUWER)

These regulations cover all new or existing work equipment – leased, hired or second-hand. They apply in most working environments where the HSW applies, including all industrial, offshore and service operations.

PUWER covers starting, stopping, regular use, transport, repair, modification, servicing and cleaning.

'Work equipment' includes any machinery, appliance, apparatus or tool, and any assembly of components that are used in non-domestic premises. Dumper trucks, circular saws, ladders, overhead projectors and chisels would all be included, but substances, private cars and structural items all fall outside this definition.

The general duties of the act require equipment to be:

- suitable for its intended purpose and only to be used in suitable conditions
- maintained in an efficient state and maintenance records kept
- used, repaired and maintained only by a suitably trained person, when that equipment poses a particular risk
- able to be isolated from all its sources of energy
- constructed or adapted to ensure that maintenance can be carried out without risks to health and safety
- fitted with warnings or warning devices as appropriate.

In addition, the act requires:

- all those who use, supervise or manage work equipment to be suitably trained
- access to any dangerous parts of the machinery to be prevented or controlled
- injury to be prevented from any work equipment that may have a very high or low temperature
- suitable controls to be provided for starting and stopping the work equipment
- suitable emergency stopping systems and braking systems to be fitted to ensure the work equipment is brought to a safe condition as soon as reasonably practicable
- suitable and sufficient lighting to be provided for operating the work equipment.

Control of Substances Hazardous to Health Regulations 2002 (COSHH)

These regulations state how employees and employers should work with, handle, store, transport and dispose of potentially hazardous substances (substances that might negatively affect your health) including:

- substances used directly in work activities (e.g. adhesives or paints)
- substances generated during work activities (e.g. dust from sanding wood)
- naturally occurring substances (e.g. sand dust)
- biological agents (e.g. bacteria).

Hazardous substances

These substances can be found in nearly all work environments. All are covered by COSHH regulations except asbestos and lead paint, which have their own regulations.

To comply with COSHH regulations, eight steps must be followed:

Step 1 Assess the risks to health from hazardous substances used or created by your activities.

Step 2 Decide what precautions are needed.

Step 3 Prevent employees from being exposed to any hazardous substances. If prevention is impossible, the risk must be adequately controlled.

Step 4 Ensure control methods are used and maintained properly.

Step 5 Monitor the exposure of employees to hazardous substances.

Step 6 Carry out health **surveillance** to ascertain if any health problems are occurring.

Step 7 Prepare plans and procedures to deal with accidents such as spillages.

Step 8 Ensure all employees are properly informed, trained and supervised.

Safety tip

Not all substances are labelled, and sometimes the label may not match the contents. If you are in any doubt, do not use or touch the substance

Identifying a substance that may fall under the COSHH regulations is not always easy, but you can ask the supplier or manufacturer for a COSHH data sheet, outlining the risks involved with it. Most substance containers carry a warning sign stating whether the contents are corrosive, harmful, toxic or bad for the environment.

As you can see, supervision is specifically mentioned in Step 8 above. For the Level 3 candidate, this may mean a much greater and more active involvement in compliance with COSHH regulations: you may become a doer – carrying out training, overseeing others and even carrying out some of the previous steps on behalf of your employer – rather than just a receiver of information and guidance.

Common safety signs for corrosive, toxic and harmful materials

The Personal Protective Equipment at Work Regulations 1992 (PPER)

These regulations cover all types of PPE, from gloves to breathing apparatus. After doing a risk assessment and once the potential hazards are known, suitable types of PPE can be selected. PPE should be checked prior to issue by a trained and competent person and in line with the manufacturer's instructions. Where required, the employer must provide PPE free of charge along with a suitable and secure place to store it.

Remember

PPE must only be used as a last line of defence

The employer must ensure that the employee knows:

- the risks the PPE will avoid or reduce
- its purpose and use
- how to maintain and look after it
- its limitations.

The employee must:

- ensure that they are trained in the use of the PPE prior to use
- use it in line with the employer's instructions
- return it to storage after use
- take care of it, and report any loss or defect to their employer.

As with many areas of health and safety, as a Level 3 candidate you may find yourself in a position somewhere between employer and employee, supervising the work of others where PPE is in use. As a supervisor, you may not carry any direct legal responsibilities under the PPER legislation, but your employer would still be looking for you to support them in meeting these obligations, and would be looking to you to set the standards for others. At the same time, you would be obliged to look after yourself as an employee under the terms of the legislation and keep yourself safe!

The Control of Noise at Work Regulations 2005

At some point in your career in construction, you are likely to work in a noisy working environment. These regulations help protect you against the consequences of being exposed to high levels of noise, which can lead to permanent hearing damage.

Noise at work

Damage to hearing has a range of causes, from ear infections to loud noises, but the regulations deal mainly with the latter. Hearing loss can result from one very loud noise lasting only a few seconds, or from relatively loud noise lasting for hours, such as a drill.

The regulations state that the employer must:

- assess the risks to the employee from noise at work
- take action to reduce the noise exposure that produces these risks
- provide employees with hearing protection or, if this is impossible, reduce the risk by other methods
- make sure the legal limits on noise exposure are not exceeded
- provide employees with information, instruction and training
- carry out health surveillance where there is a risk to health.

Anyone who is supervising the work of others may be asked to (or may wish to) monitor noise levels in the work area and advise the employer if any problems arise from excessive noise exposure.

Did you know?

Noise is measured in **decibels (dB)**. The average person may notice a rise of 3dB, but with every 3dB rise, the noise is doubled. What may seem like a small rise is actually very significant

Remember

Hearing loss affects the young as well as the old

The Work at Height Regulations 2005

Construction workers often work high off the ground, on scaffolding, ladders or roofs. These regulations make sure that employers do all that they can to reduce the risk of injury or death from working at height.

The employer has a duty to:

- avoid work at height where possible
- use any equipment or safeguards that will prevent falls
- use equipment and any other methods that will minimise the distance and consequences of a fall.

As an employee, you must follow any training given to you, report any hazards to your supervisor and use any safety equipment made available to you. As a supervisor, you would need to understand the duties of both employer and employee, being aware that staff under your supervision should never be put in danger by failing to meet the standards required.

The Electricity at Work Regulations 1989

These regulations cover any work involving the use of electricity or electrical equipment. An employer has the duty to ensure that the electrical systems their employees come into contact with are safe and regularly maintained. They must also have done everything the law states to reduce the risk of their employees coming into contact with live electrical currents.

The Manual Handling Operations Regulations 1992

These regulations cover all work activities in which a person does the lifting rather than a machine. They state that, wherever possible, manual handling should be avoided, but where this is unavoidable, a risk assessment should be done.

In a risk assessment, there are four considerations:

- *Load* – is it heavy, sharp-edged, difficult to hold?
- *Individual* – is the individual small, pregnant, in need of training?
- *Task* – does the task require holding goods away from the body, or repetitive twisting?
- *Environment* – is the floor uneven, are there stairs, is it raining?

After the assessment, the situation must be monitored constantly and updated or changed if necessary.

The Reporting of Injuries, Diseases and Dangerous Occurrences Regulations 1995 (RIDDOR)

Under RIDDOR, employers have a duty to report accidents, diseases or dangerous occurrences. The HSE use this information to identify where and how risk arises and to investigate serious accidents.

Other acts to be aware of

You should also be aware of the following pieces of legislation:

- The Fire Precautions (Workplace) Regulations 1997
- The Fire Precautions Act 1991
- The Highly Flammable Liquids and Liquid Petroleum Gases Regulations 1972
- The Lifting Operations and Lifting Equipment Regulations 1998
- The Construction (Health, Safety and Welfare) Regulations 1996
- The Environmental Protection Act 1990
- The Confined Spaces Regulations 1997
- The Working Time Regulations 1998
- The Health and Safety (First Aid) Regulations 1981
- The Construction (Design and Management) Regulations 1994.

You can find out more at the library or online.

Find out

Look into the other regulations listed here via the Government website www.hse.gov.uk

Health and welfare

As a worker in the construction industry, you will be at constant risk unless you adopt a good health and safety attitude. By following the rules and regulations, and by taking reasonable care of yourself and others – especially where acting as a supervisor – you will become a safe worker and reduce the chance of injuries and accidents. Given the statistics on safety, the supervisor's role is crucial here: few other people will be in a better position to understand the day-to-day work of a site, be in touch with those doing the labour and spot 'danger points' where accidents or ill health could occur.

The two most common risks to a construction worker

Accidents

We often hear the saying 'accidents will happen', but in the construction industry, the truth is that most accidents are caused by human error – someone does something they shouldn't or, just as importantly, does not do something they should. Accidents often happen when someone is hurrying, not paying attention, trying to cut corners or costs, or has not received the correct training.

If an accident happens, you or the person it happened to may be lucky enough to escape uninjured. More often, an accident will result in an injury, whether minor (e.g. a cut or a bruise), major (e.g. loss of a limb) or even fatal. The most common causes of fatal accidents in the construction industry are:

- falling from scaffolding
- being hit by falling materials
- falling through fragile roofs
- being hit by a forklift or lorry
- **electrocution**.

Ill health

In the construction industry, you will be exposed to substances or situations that may be harmful to your health. Some of these health risks may not be noticeable straight away and it may take years for symptoms to be noticed and recognised. Ill health can result from:

- exposure to dust (e.g. asbestos) – breathing problems and cancer
- exposure to **solvents** or chemicals – dermatitis and other skin problems
- lifting heavy or difficult loads – back injury and pulled muscles
- exposure to loud noise – hearing problems and deafness
- using vibrating tools – **vibration white finger** and other hand problems.

A fall could be fatal

Remember

Everyone has a responsibility for health and safety, but accidents and health problems still happen too often. Make sure you do what you can to prevent them

Staying healthy

As well as watching for hazards, you must also look after yourself and stay healthy.

One of the easiest ways to do this is to wash your hands regularly: this prevents hazardous substances entering your body through ingestion (swallowing). You should always wash your hands after going to the toilet and before eating or drinking.

You can also make sure that you wear barrier cream and the correct PPE, and only drink water that is labelled as drinking water.

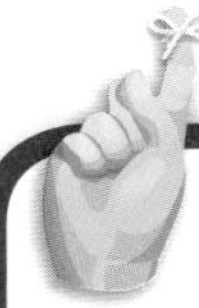

Remember

Some health problems do not show symptoms straight away – and what you do now can affect you greatly in later life

Welfare facilities

Welfare facilities are things that an employer must provide to ensure a safe and healthy workplace.

- **Toilets** – The number provided depends on how many people are intending to use them. Males and females can use the same toilet providing the door can be locked from the inside. Toilets should ideally be flushable with water or, if this is not possible, with chemicals.
- **Washing facilities** – Employers must provide a basin large enough for people to wash their hands, face and forearms, with hot and cold running water, soap and a way to dry your hands. Showers may be needed if the work is very dirty or if workers are exposed to toxic or corrosive substances.
- **Drinking water** – A supply of clean drinking water should be available, from a mains-linked tap or bottled water. Mains-linked taps need to be clearly labelled as drinking water; bottled drinking water must be stored where there is no chance of contamination.
- **Storage or dry room** – Every building site must have an area where workers can store clothes not worn on site, such as coats and motorcycle helmets. If this area is to be used as a drying room, adequate heating must be provided.
- **Lunch area** – Every site must have facilities for taking breaks and lunch well away from the work area. There must be shelter from the wind and rain, with heating as required, along with tables and chairs, a kettle or urn and a means of heating food.

Did you know?

We all carry out risk assessments hundreds of times a day. For example, every time we boil a kettle, we do a risk assessment without even thinking about it: for example, by checking the kettle isn't too full, or the cable frayed, and by keeping children out of the way

Risk assessments

You will have noticed that most of the legislation we have looked at requires risk assessments to be carried out. The Management of Health and Safety at Work Regulations 1999 require every employer to make suitable and sufficient assessment of:

- the risks to the health and safety of his/her employees to which they are exposed while at work
- the risks to the health and safety of persons not in his/her employment arising out of or in connection with his/her work activities.

Definition

Making a risk assessment – measuring the dangers of an activity against the likelihood of accidents taking place.

As a Level 3 candidate, it is vital that you know how to carry out a risk assessment. Often you may be in a position where you are given direct responsibility for this, and the care and attention you take over it may have a direct impact on the safety of others. You must be aware of the dangers or hazards of any task, and know what can be done to prevent or reduce the risk.

There are five steps in a risk assessment – here we use cutting the grass as an example:

Even an everyday task like cutting the grass has its own dangers

Step 1 Identify the hazards

When cutting the grass the main hazards are from the blades or cutting the wire, electrocution and any stones that may be thrown up.

Step 2 Identify who will be at risk

The main person at risk is the user but passers-by may be struck by flying debris.

Step 3 Calculate the risk from the hazard against the likelihood of an accident taking place

The risks from the hazard are quite high: the blade or wire can remove a finger, electrocution can kill and the flying debris can blind or even kill. The likelihood of an accident happening is medium: you are unlikely to cut yourself on the blades, but the chance of cutting through the cable is medium, and the chance of hitting a stone high.

Step 4 Introduce measures to reduce the risk

Training can reduce the risks of cutting yourself; training and the use of an **RCD** can reduce the risk of electrocution; and raking the lawn first can reduce the risk of sending up stones.

Step 5 Monitor the risk

Constantly changing factors mean any risk assessment may have to be modified or even changed completely. In our example, one such factor could be rain.

Definition

RCD – residual current device, a device that will shut the power down on a piece of electrical equipment if it detects a change in the current, thus preventing electrocution

On the job: Causing a hazard

Danielle and Stephanie are working on a building site laying upper floor chipboard flooring, with Danielle acting as supervisor. At lunchtime they both rush off leaving the area unsupervised. Roger walks over to borrow a nail gun and when he steps on what seems to be a fixed board, the board flips up. Roger falls down to the next level, seriously injuring himself. Who do you think is to blame? What would you have done in the circumstances?

FAQ

What is the difference between being an employee and being a supervisor when it comes to health and safety?

As a supervisor, you need to be aware of the different pieces of legislation and consider them when you are overseeing other people's work. You may be given responsibility to help your employer comply with their part of legislation too.

How do I find out what safety legislation is relevant to my job?

Ask your employer or contact the HSE at www.hse.gov.uk.

How do I find my company's safety policy?

Ask your supervisor or employer.

When do I need to do a risk assessment?

A risk assessment should be carried out if there is any chance of an accident happening. To be on the safe side, you should make a risk assessment before starting each task.

Do I need to read and understand every regulation?

No. It is part of your employer's duty to ensure that you are aware of what you need to know.

Knowledge check

1. What is legislation?
2. What is an approved code of practice?
3. What is the purpose of a safety policy?
4. What does '*so far as is reasonably practicable*' mean?
5. Who enforces the health and safety regulations?
6. State three of the main objectives of the Health and Safety at Work Act 1974.
7. State four duties included in the PUWER regulations.
8. List three things that can cause ill health, and what health problems they can create.
9. State five welfare facilities that *must* be made available.
10. What is the purpose of a risk assessment?
11. Name three ways in which a supervisor's role with health and safety differs from an ordinary employee?

chapter 2

Building documentation

OVERVIEW

In the construction industry you come across a wide range of documentation, and as a Level 3 apprentice you will encounter different types of documents more frequently. This chapter covers the main building documentation you will see, explaining what each type of documentation is and what it is used for. The types of documentation covered in this chapter are:

- plans and drawings
- contract documents
- Building Regulations documentation
- general site paperwork.

Plans and drawings

Definition

The Building Regulations – a set of regulations brought in to deal with poor housing conditions, which now restrict what can be built, how and where. For more details, see Chapter 3, pages 40–42

Plans and drawings are vital to any building work as a way of expressing the client's wishes. Drawings are the best way of communicating a lot of detailed information without the need for pages and pages of text. Drawings form part of the contract documents (which will be explained later) and go through several stages before they are given to tradespeople for use.

Stage 1 The client sits down with an architect and explains his/her requirements.

Stage 2 The architect produces drawings of the work and checks with the client to see if the drawings match what the client wants.

Stage 3 If required, the drawings go to planning to see if they can be allowed, and are also scrutinised by **the Building Regulations** Authority. It is at this stage that the drawings may need to be altered to meet Planning or Building Regulations.

Stage 4 Once passed, the drawings are given to contractors along with the other contract documents, so that they can prepare their tenders for the contract.

Stage 5 The winning contractor uses the drawings to carry out the job. At this point the drawings will be given to you to work from.

There are three main types of working drawings: location drawings, component drawings and assembly drawings. We will look at each of these in turn.

Location drawings

Location drawings include:

- **block plans**, which identify the proposed site in relation to the surrounding area. These are usually drawn at a scale of 1:2500 or 1:1250

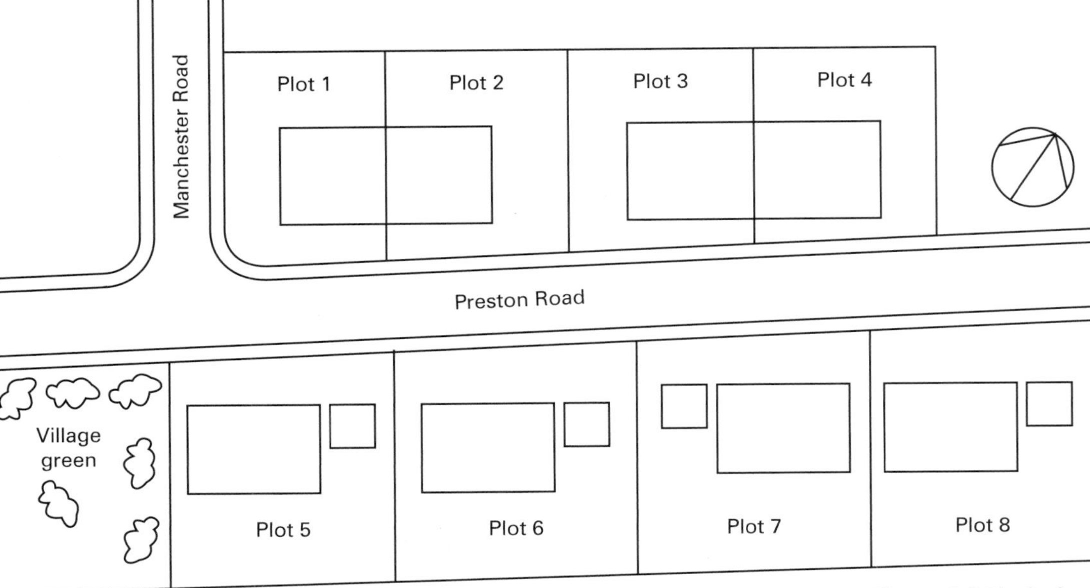

Figure 2.1 Block plan

- **site plans**, which give the position of the proposed building and the general layout of things such as services and drainage. These are usually drawn at a scale of 1:500 or 1:200

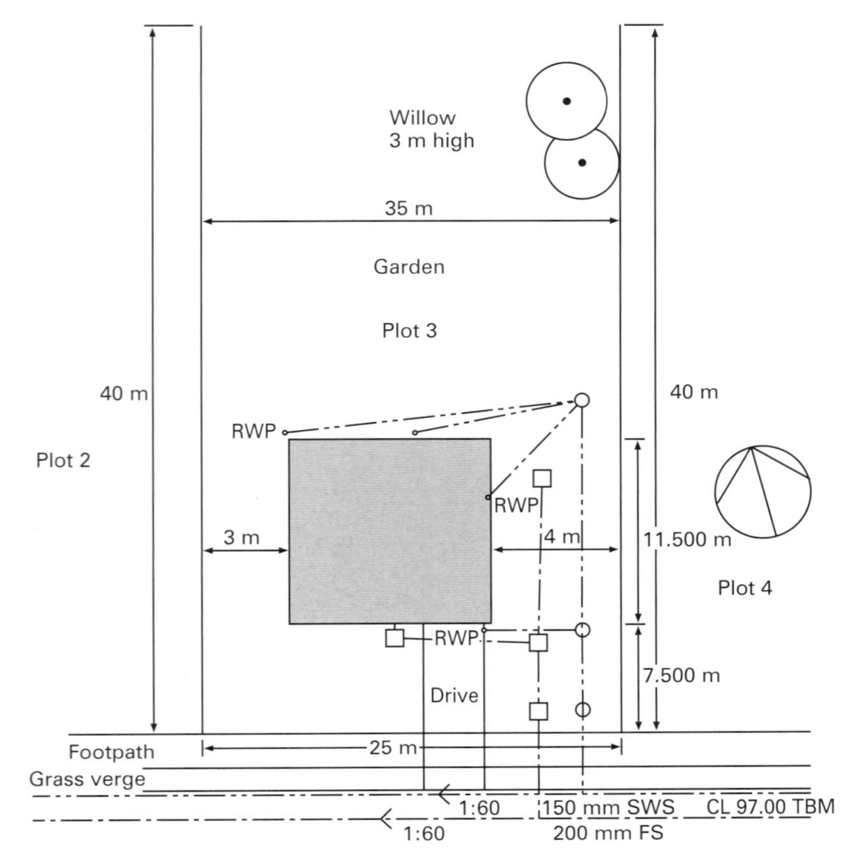

Figure 2.2 Site plan

- **general location drawings**, which show different elevations and sections of the building. These are usually drawn at a scale of 1:200, 1:100 or 1:50

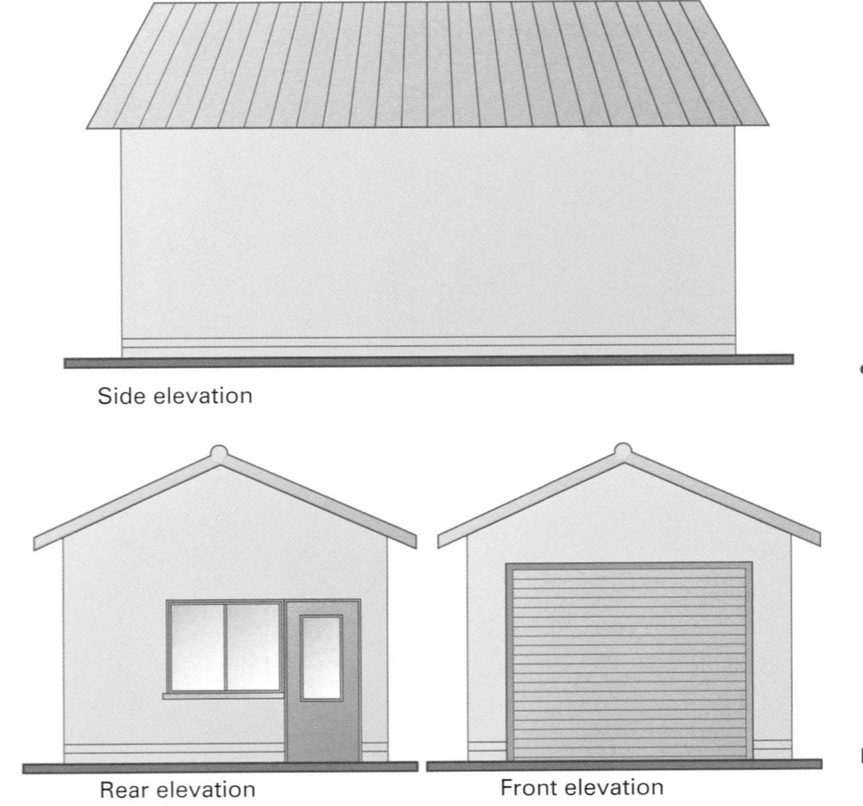

Figure 2.3 General location drawing

Component drawings

Component drawings include:

- **range drawings**, which show the different sizes and shapes of a particular range of components. These are usually drawn at a scale of 1:50 or 1:20

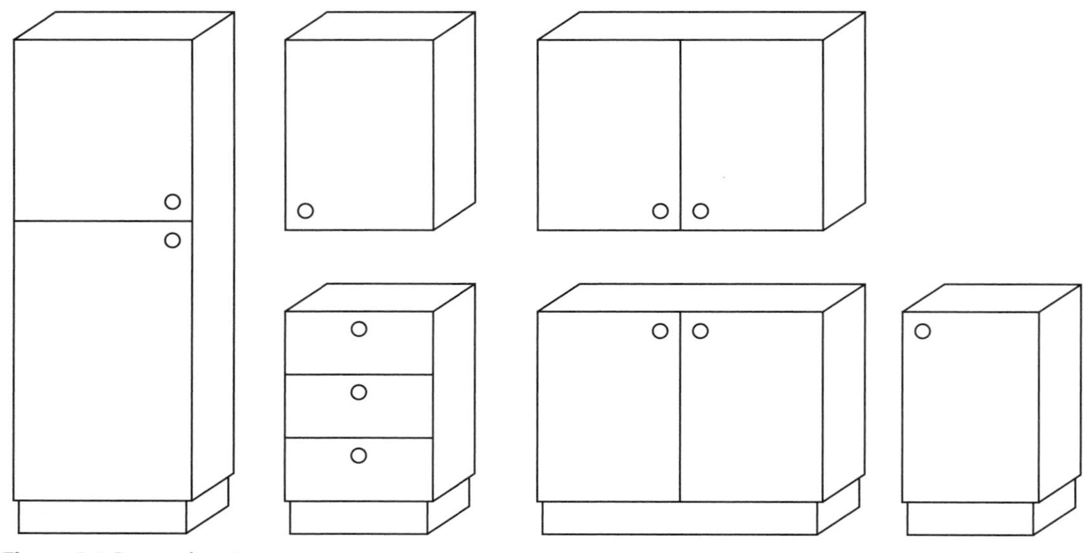

Figure 2.4 Range drawing

- **detailed drawings**, which show all the information needed to complete or manufacture a component. These are usually drawn at a scale of 1:10, 1:5 or 1:1.

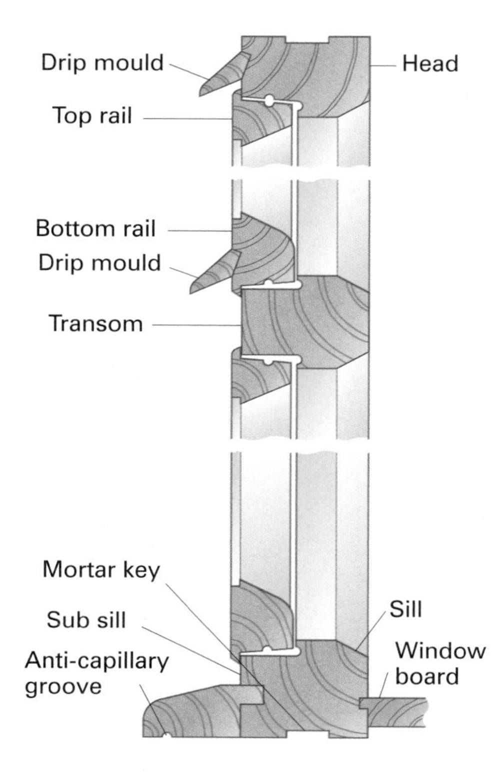

Figure 2.5 Detailed drawing

Assembly drawings

Assembly drawings are similar to detailed drawings and show in great detail the various joints and junctions in and between the various parts and components of a building. Assembly drawings are usually drawn at a scale of 1:20, 1:10 or 1:5.

All plans and drawings contain symbols and abbreviations, which are used to show the maximum amount of information in a clear and legible way.

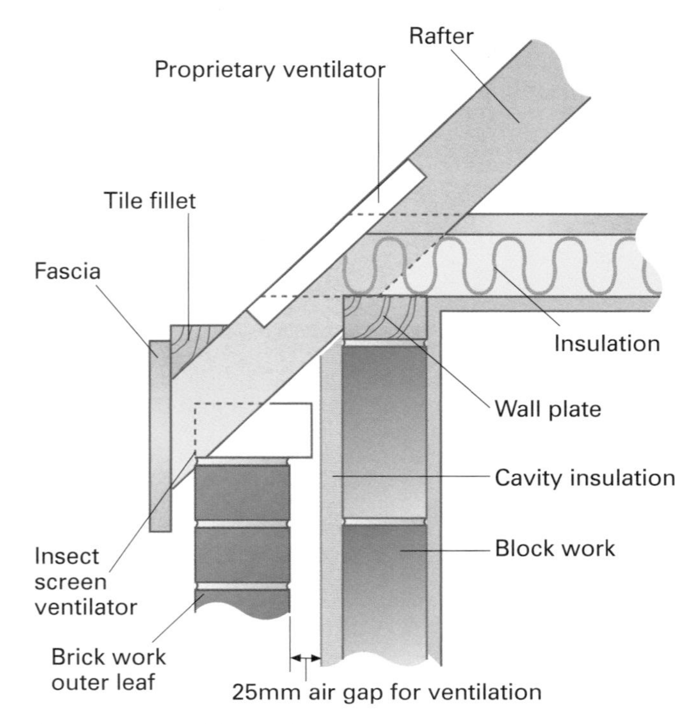

Figure 2.6 Assembly drawing

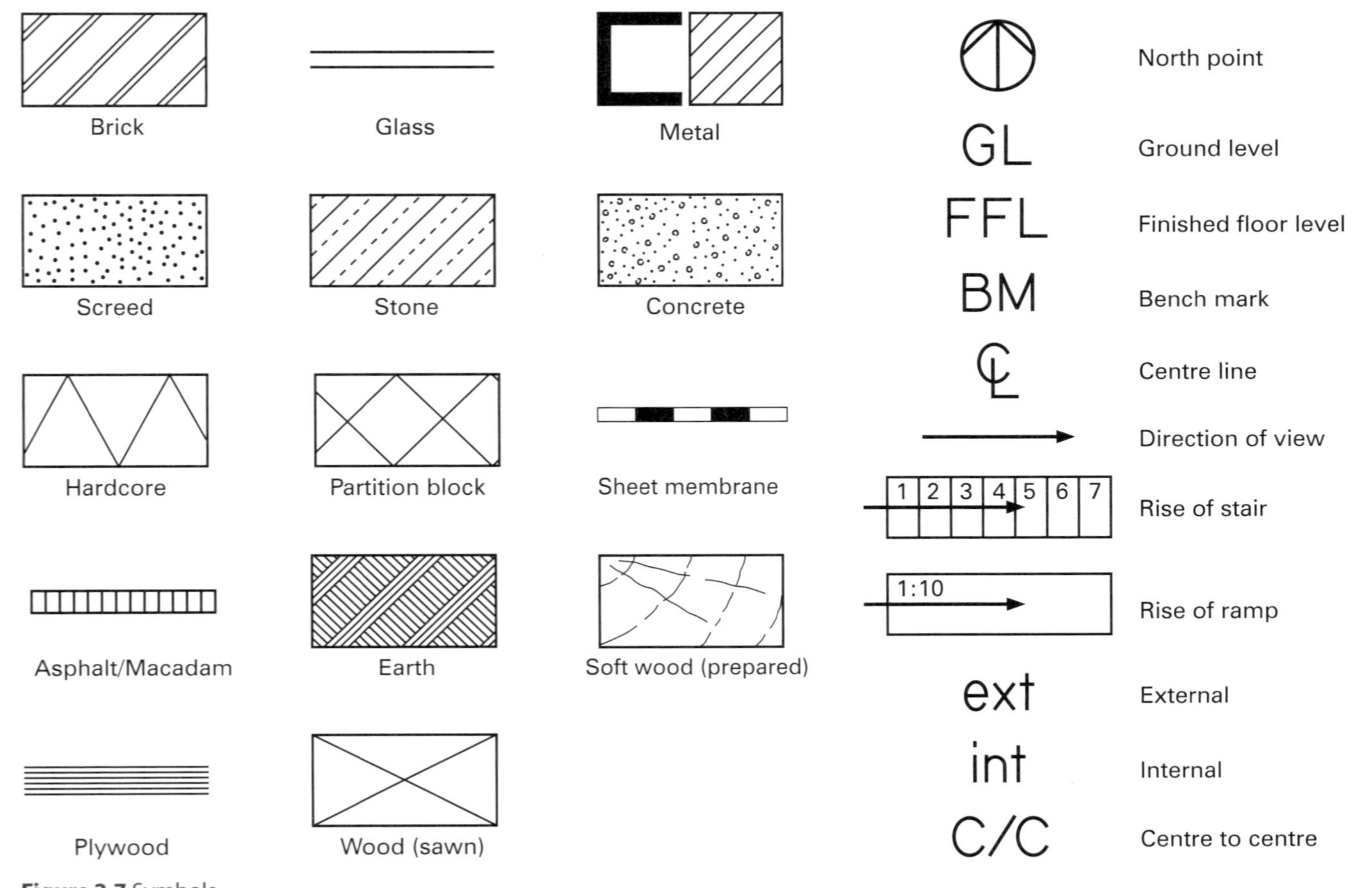

Figure 2.7 Symbols

Item	Abbreviation	Item	Abbreviation
Airbrick	AB	Hardcore	hc
Asbestos	abs	Hardwood	hwd
Bitumen	bit	Insulation	insul
Boarding	bdg	Joist	jst
Brickwork	bwk	Mild steel	MS
Building	bldg	Plasterboard	pbd
Cast iron	CI	Polyvinyl acetate	PVA
Cement	ct	Polyvinyl chloride	PVC
Column	col	Reinforced concrete	RC
Concrete	conc	Satin chrome	SC
Cupboard	cpd	Satin anodised aluminium	SAA
Damp proof course	DPC	Softwood	swd
Damp proof membrane	DPM	Stainless steel	SS
Drawing	dwg	Tongue and groove	T&G
Foundation	fnd	Wrought iron	WI
Hardboard	hdbd		

Table 2.1 Abbreviations

Contract documents

Contract documents are also vital to a construction project. They are created by a team of specialists – the architect, structural engineer, services engineer and quantity surveyor – who first look at the draft of drawings from the architect and client. Just which contract documents this team goes on to produce will vary depending on the size and type of work being done, but will usually include:

- plans and drawings
- specification
- schedules
- bill of quantities
- conditions of contract.

Plans and drawings have already been covered, so here we will start with the specification.

Specification

The specification or 'spec' is a document produced alongside the plans and drawings and is used to show information that cannot be shown on the drawings. Specifications are almost always used, except in the case of very small contracts. A specification should contain:

- **site description** – a brief description of the site including the address
- **restrictions** – what restrictions apply such as working hours or limited access
- **services** – what services are available, what services need to be connected and what type of connection should be used
- **materials description** – including type, sizes, quality, moisture content etc.
- **workmanship** – including methods of fixing, quality of work and finish.

A good 'spec' helps avoid confusion when dealing with sub-contractors or suppliers

The specification may also name sub-contractors or suppliers, or give details such as how the site should be cleared, and so on.

An example of a specification can be found in the fictional project in Chapter 4 (see page 59).

Schedules

A schedule is used to record repeated design information that applies to a range of components or fittings. Schedules are mainly used on bigger sites where there are multiples of several types of house (4-bedroom, 3-bedroom, 3-bedroom with dormers, etc.), each type having different components and fittings. The schedule avoids the wrong component or fitting being put in the wrong house. Schedules can also be used on smaller jobs such as a block of flats with 200 windows, where there are six different types of window.

The need for a specification depends on the complexity of the job and the number of repeated designs that there are. Schedules are mainly used to record repeated design information for:

- doors
- windows
- ironmongery
- joinery fitments
- sanitary components
- heating components and radiators
- kitchens.

A schedule is usually used in conjunction with a range drawing and a floor plan.

The following are basic examples of these documents, using a window as an example:

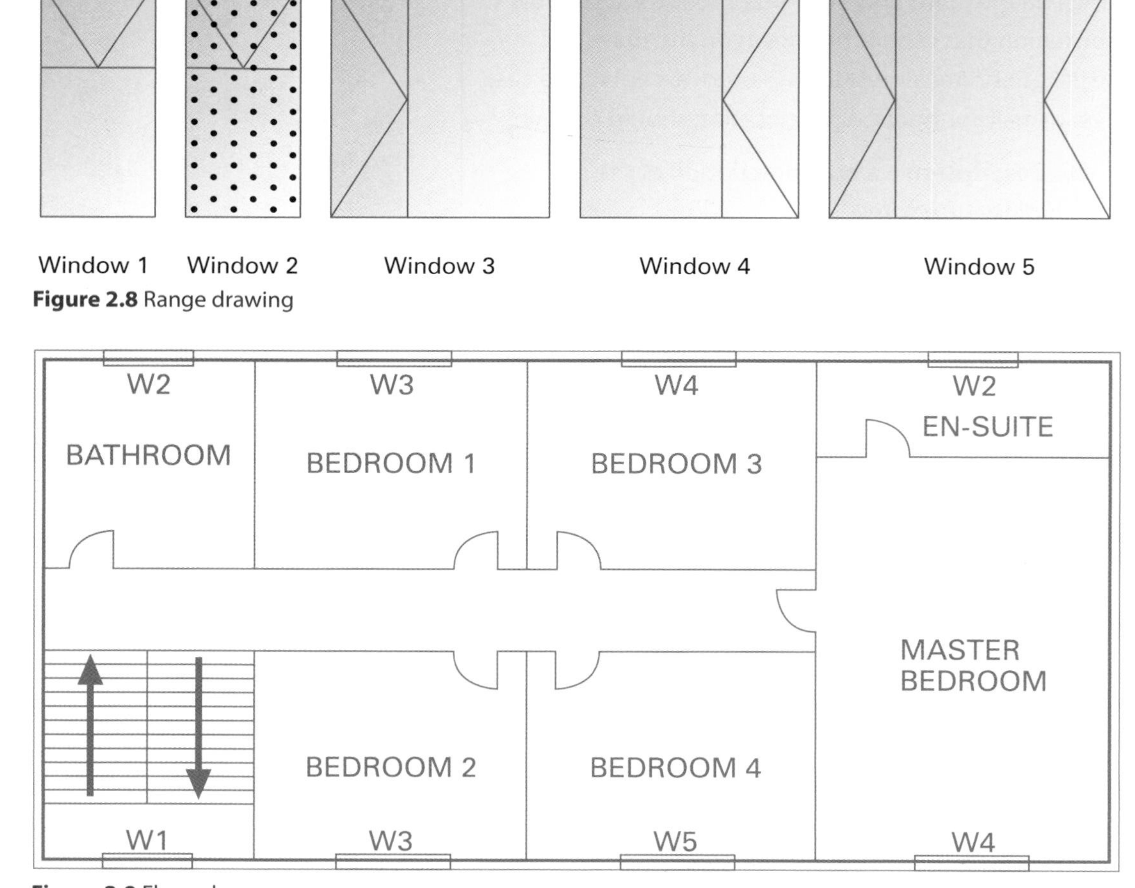

Figure 2.8 Range drawing

Figure 2.9 Floor plan

WINDOW SCHEDULE		
WINDOW	LOCATIONS	NOTES
Window 1	Stairwell	
Window 2	Bathroom En-suite	Obscure glass
Window 3	Bedroom 1 Bedroom 2	
Window 4	Bedroom 3 Master bedroom	
Window 5	Bedroom 4	

Figure 2.10 Schedule for a window

The schedule shows that there are five types of window, each differing in size and appearance; the range drawing shows what each type of window looks like; and the floor plan shows which window goes where. For example, the bathroom window is a type two window, which is 1200 × 600 × 50cm with a top-opening sash and obscure glass.

Bill of quantities

The bill of quantities is produced by the quantity surveyor. It gives a complete description of everything that is required to do the job, including labour, materials and any items or components, drawing on information from the drawings, specification and schedule. The same single bill of quantities is sent out to all **prospective** contractors so they can submit a tender based on the same information – this helps the client select the best contractor for the job.

Every item needed should be listed on the bill of quantities

All bills of quantities contain the following information:

- **preliminaries** – general information such as the names of the client and architect, details of the work and descriptions of the site
- **preambles** – similar to the specification, outlining the quality and description of materials and workmanship, etc.
- **measured quantities** – a description of how each task or material is measured with measurements in metres (linear and square), hours, litres, kilograms or simply the number of components required
- **provisional quantities** – approximate amounts where items or components cannot be measured accurately
- **cost** – the amount of money that will be charged per unit of quantity.

The bill of quantities may also contain:

- any costs that may result from using sub-contractors or specialists
- a sum of money for work that has not been finally detailed
- a sum of money to cover contingencies for unforeseen work.

This is an extract from a bill of quantities that might be sent to prospective contractors, who would then complete the cost section and return it as their tender.

Item ref No	Description	Quantity	Unit	Rate £	Cost £
A1	'Tudor Grange' smooth face red rustic brick (Class B)	11,000	1,000		
A2	100mm Aircrete	1,750	100		
C1	Pre-mixed sand cement mortar (1:4)	13,750	tonne		
D1	Galvanised steel cavity wall ties (Butterfly)	2,200	200		

Figure 2.11 Sample extract from a bill of quantities

To ensure that all contractors interpret and understand the bill of quantities consistently, the Royal Institution of Chartered Surveyors and the Building Employers' Confederation produce a document called the *Standard Method of Measurement of Building Works* (SMM). This provides a uniform basis for measuring building work, for example stating that carcassing timber is measured by the metre whereas plasterboard is measured in square metres.

Conditions of contract

Almost all building work is carried out under a contract. A small job with a single client (e.g. a loft conversion) will have a basic contract stating that the contractor will do the work to the client's satisfaction, and that the client will pay the contractor the agreed sum of money once the work is finished. Larger contracts with clients such as the Government will have additional clauses, terms or **stipulations**, which may include any of the following.

Variations

A variation is a modification of the original drawing or specification. The architect or client must give the contractor written confirmation of the variation, then the contractor submits a price for the variation to the quantity surveyor (or client, on a small job). Once the price is accepted, the variation work can be completed.

Did you know?

On a poorly run contract, a penalty clause can be very costly and could incur a substantial payment. In an extreme case, the contractor may end up making a loss instead of a profit on the project

Interim payment

An **interim** payment schedule may be written into the contract, meaning that the client pays for the work in instalments. The client may pay an amount each month, linked to how far the job has progressed, or may make regular payments regardless of how far the job has progressed.

Final payment

Here the client makes a one-off full payment once the job has been completed to the specification. A final payment scheme may also have additional clauses included, such as:

- **retention**
  This is when the client holds a small percentage of the full payment back for a specified period (usually six months). It may take some time for any defects to show, such as cracks in plaster. If the contractor fixes the defects, they will receive the retention payment; if they don't fix them, the retention payment can be used to hire another contractor to do so.
- **penalty clause**
  This is usually introduced in contracts with a tight deadline, where the building must be finished and ready to operate on time. If the project overruns, the client will be unable to trade in the premises and will lose money, so the contractor will have to compensate the client for lost revenue.

Find out

For more about the Building Regulations, visit www.ukbuildingstandards.org.uk

Remember

Building regulations can change over time. Always be sure you are using the most updated version.

Building Regulations documentation

Building Regulations are a set of rulings that apply to many construction projects, and are linked with a whole range of documentation that you may come across in your job.

The background to the Building Regulations is covered in detail in Chapter 3, but here we will focus on the actual documents you need to know about.

The regulations are broken down into several categories:

- Part A – Structural safety
- Part B – Fire safety
- Part C – Resistance to moisture and weather
- Part D – Toxic substances
- Part E – Resistance to sound
- Part F – Ventilation
- Part G – Hygiene
- Part H – Drainage and waste disposal
- Part J – Heat-producing appliances
- Part K – Protection from falling
- Part L – Conservation of fuel and power
- Part M – Access to and use of buildings
- Part N – Glazing safety
- Part P – Electrical safety.

Each of these sections contains an 'approved document', detailing what is covered by that part of the regulations:

Approved document A

A1 – Loading

A2 – Ground movement

A3 – Disproportionate collapse

Approved document B

B1 – Means of warning and escape

B2 – Internal fire spread (linings)

B3 – Internal fire spread (structure)

B4 – External fire spread

B5 – Access and facilities for the fire service

Approved document C

C1 – Site preparation and resistance to contaminates

C2 – Resistance to moisture

Approved document D

D1 – Cavity insulation

Approved document E

E1 – Protection against sound from other parts of the building and adjoining buildings

E2 – Protection against sound within a dwelling-house, etc.

E3 – Reverberation in the common internal parts of buildings containing flats or rooms for residential purposes

E4 – Acoustic conditions in schools

Approved document F deals only with ventilation

Approved document G

G1 – Sanitary conveniences and washing facilities

G2 – Bathrooms

G3 – Hot water storage

Approved document H

H1 – Foul water drainage

H2 – Wastewater treatment systems and cesspools

H3 – Rainwater drainage

H4 – Building over sewers

H5 – Separate systems of drainage

H6 – Solid waste storage

Approved document J

J1 – Air supply

J2 – Discharge of products of combustion

J3 – Protection of building

J4 – Provision of information

J5 – Protection of liquid fuel storage systems

J6 – Protection against pollution

Approved document K

K1 – Stairs, ladders and ramps

K2 – Protection from falling

K3 – Vehicle barriers and loading bays

K4 – Protection from collision with open windows, skylights and ventilators

K5 – Protection against impact from and trapping by doors

Approved document L

L1A – Conservation of fuel and power in new dwellings

L1B – Conservation of fuel and power in existing dwellings

L2A – Conservation of fuel and power in new buildings other than dwellings

L2B – Conservation of fuel and power in existing buildings other than dwellings

Approved document M

M1 – Access and use

M2 – Access to extensions to buildings other than dwellings

M3 – Sanitary conveniences in extensions to buildings other than dwellings

M4 – Sanitary conveniences in dwellings

Approved document N

N1 – Protection against impact

N2 – Manifestation of glazing

N3 – Safe opening and closing of windows, skylights and ventilators

N4 – Safe access for cleaning windows, etc.

Approved document P

P1 – Design and installation of electrical installations

Almost all building work requires approval from the Building Regulations Authority. The few exemptions include greenhouses or agricultural buildings, which fall outside parts A–K, M and N, and agricultural buildings, which are also exempt from part P. Some of these may still require planning permission.

General site paperwork

No building site could function properly without a certain amount of paperwork. Here is a brief, but not exhaustive, description of some of the other documents you may encounter. Some companies will have their own forms to cover such things as scaffolding checks.

Timesheet

Timesheets record hours worked, and are completed by every employee individually. Some timesheets are basic, asking just for a brief description of the work done each hour, but some can be complicated. In some cases timesheets may be used to work out how many hours the client will be charged for.

P. Gresford Building Contractors

Timesheet

Employee ______________________ **Project/site** ______________________

Date	Job no.	Start time	Finish time	Total time	Travel time	Expenses
M						
Tu						
W						
Th						
F						
Sa						
Su						

Totals						

Employee's signature ______________________

Supervisor's signature ______________________

Date ______________________

Figure 2.12 Timesheet

Day worksheets

Day worksheets are often confused with timesheets, but are different as they are used when there is no price or estimate for the work, to enable the contractor to charge for the work. Day worksheets record work done, hours worked and sometimes materials used.

P. Gresford Building Contractors

Day worksheet

Customer Chris MacFarlane Date

Description of work being carried out

Install catnic lintel above kitchen window.

Construct soldier course above lintel.

Labour	Craft	Hours	Gross rate	TOTALS
Materials	Quantity	Rate	% addition	
Plant	Hours	Rate	% addition	

Comments

Signed Date

Site manager/foreman signature

Figure 2.13 Day worksheet

P. Gresford Building Contractors

Job sheet

Customer Chris MacFarlane

Address 1 High Street
Any Town
Any County

Work to be carried out

Install catnic lintel above kitchen window
Construct soldier course above lintel

Special conditions/instructions

Lintel to be 150mm bearing either side of opening
Soldier course to be of blue engineering bricks – supplied on site

Figure 2.14 Job sheet

Job sheet

A job sheet is similar to a day worksheet – it records work done – but is used when the work has already been priced. Job sheets enable the worker to see what needs to be done and the site agent or working foreman to see what has been completed.

Variation order

This sheet is used by the architect to make any changes to the original plans, including omissions, alterations and extra work.

VARIATION TO PROPOSED WORKS AT 123 A STREET

REFERENCE NO:

DATE ______________________

FROM ______________________

TO ______________________

POSSIBLE VARIATIONS TO WORK AT 123 A STREET

ADDITIONS
OMISSIONS

SIGNED ------------------------------------

Figure 2.15 Variation order

Confirmation notice

This is a sheet given to the contractor to confirm any changes made in the variation order, so that the contractor can go ahead and carry out the work.

CONFIRMATION FOR VARIATION TO PROPOSED WORKS AT 123 A STREET

REFERENCE NO:

DATE ______________________

FROM ______________________

TO ______________________

I CONFIRM THAT I HAVE RECEIVED WRITTEN INSTRUCTIONS
FROM ______________________
POSITION ______________________
TO CARRY OUT THE FOLLOWING POSSIBLE VARIATIONS TO THE ABOVE NAMED CONTRACT

ADDITIONS
OMISSIONS

SIGNED ------------------------------------

Figure 2.16 Confirmation notice

Orders/requisitions

A requisition form or order is used to order materials or components from a supplier.

P. Gresford Building Contractors

Requisition form

Supplier ______________________ Order no. ______________

______________________ Serial no. ______________

Tel no. ______________________ Contact ______________

Fax no. ______________________ Our ref ______________

Contract/Delivery address/Invoice address ______________________ Statements/applications for payments to be sent to ______________

Tel no. ______________________

Fax no. ______________________

Item no.	Quantity	Unit	Description	Unit price	Amount

Total £ ______________

Payment terms ______________ Date ______________

Originated by ______________________

Authorised by ______________________

Figure 2.17 Requisition form

Delivery notes

Delivery notes are given to the contractor by the supplier, and list all the materials and components being delivered. Each delivery note should be checked for accuracy against the order (to ensure what is being delivered is what was asked for) and against the delivery itself (to make sure that the delivery matches the delivery note). If there are any **discrepancies** or if the delivery is of a poor quality or damaged, you must write on the delivery note what is wrong *before* signing it and ensure the site agent is informed so that he/she can rectify the problem.

Bailey & Sons Ltd

Building materials supplier

Tel: 01234 567890

Your ref: AB00671

Our ref: CT020

Date: 17 Jul 2007

Order no: 67440387

Invoice address:
Carillion Training Centre,
Deptford Terrace, Sunderland

Delivery address:
Same as invoice

Description of goods	Quantity	Catalogue no.
OPC 25kg	10	OPC1.1

Comments:
Date and time of receiving goods:
Name of recipient (caps):
Signature:

Figure 2.18 Delivery note

Invoices

Invoices come from a variety of sources such as suppliers or sub-contractors, and state what has been provided and how much the contractor will be charged for it.

Remember

Invoices may need paying by a certain date – fines for late payment can sometimes be incurred – so it is important that they are passed on to the finance office or financial controller promptly

INVOICE

JARVIS BUILDING SUPPLIES
3rd AVENUE
THOMASTOWN

L weeks Builders
4th Grove
Thomastown

Quantity	Description	Unit price	Vat rate	Total
2 Tonnes	OPC	£160.00	17.5%	£376.00
			TOTAL	£376.00

To be paid within 30 days from receipt of this invoice

Please direct any queries to 01234 56789

Figure 2.19 Invoice

Delivery records

Delivery records list all deliveries over a certain period (usually a month), and are sent to the contractor's Head Office so that payment can be made.

JARVIS BUILDING SUPPLIES
3rd AVENUE
THOMASTOWN

Customer ref ________________

Customer order date ________________

Delivery date ________________

Item no	Qty Supplied	Qty to follow	Description	Unit price
1	2 Tonnes	0	OPC	£376.00

Delivered to: L Weeks builders
4th Grove
Thomastown

Customer signature ------------------------

Figure 2.20 Delivery record

DAILY REPORT/SITE DIARY

PROJECT ________________
DATE ________________

Identify any of the following factors, which are affecting or may affect the daily work activities and give a brief description in the box provided

WEATHER ( ) ACCESS ( ) ACCIDENTS ( ) SERVICES ( )
DELIVERIES ( ) SUPPLIES ( ) LABOUR ( ) OTHER ( )

SIGNED ------------------------
POSITION ------------------------

Figure 2.21 Daily report or site diary

Daily report/site diary

This is used to pass general information (deliveries, attendance etc.) on to a company's Head Office.

Remember

Remember – you should always check a delivery note against the order and the delivery itself, then write any discrepancies or problems on the delivery note *before* signing it

Accident and near miss reports

It is a legal requirement that a company has an accident book, in which reports of all accidents must be made. Reports must also be made when an accident nearly happened, but did not in the end occur – known as a 'near miss'. It is everyone's responsibility to complete the accident book. If you are also in a supervisory position you will have the responsibility to ensure all requirements for accident reporting are met.

Safety tip

If you are involved in or witness an accident or near miss, make sure it is entered in the book – for your own safety and that of others on the site. If you don't report it, it's more likely to happen again

Report of an Accident, Dangerous Occurrence or Near Miss

Date of incident ______________ **Time of incident** ______________

Location of incident ______________

Details of person involved in accident

Name ______________ Date of birth ______________

Address ______________

____

______________ Occupation ______________

Date off work (if applicable) ______________ **Date returning to work** ______________

Nature of injury ______________

Management of injury
☐ First Aid only ☐ Advised to see doctor
☐ Sent to casualty ☐ Admitted to hospital

Account of accident, dangerous occurrence or near miss
(Continued on separate sheet if necessary)

Witnesses to the incident
(Names, addresses and occupations)

Was the injured person wearing PPE? If yes, what PPE? ______________

____

Signature of person completing form ______________

Occupation ______________ **Date** ______________

Figure 2.22 Accident/near miss report

On the job: Complying with approvals

Brian and Amanda have been approached by a friend to do a loft conversion. They apply for Planning and Building Regulations approval and are given both, so they carry out the work. They also come across a problem with the chimney and decide to remove some of the bricks. With the work completed, the Building Inspector shows up to check the job. What can the Inspector do? What effect will this have on the job? What could have been done to prevent it?

FAQ

How do I know what scale the drawing is at?

The scale should be written on the title panel (the box included on a plan or drawing giving basic information such as who drew it, how to contact them, the date and the scale).

How do I know if I need a schedule?

Schedules are only really used in large jobs where there is a lot of repeated design information. If your job has a lot of doors, windows etc., it is a good idea to use one.

How do I know if I need approval?

If you are unsure, check section three of the Building Regulations or contact your local authority.

Do I need to know all the different Building Regulations and what is contained in each section?

No, but a good understanding of what is involved is needed.

How many different forms are there?

A lot of forms are used and some companies use more than others. You should ensure you get the relevant training on completing the form before using it.

Knowledge check

1. Who draws the plans?
2. State three different types of drawings and give a suitable scale for each one.
3. State three of the main contract documents.
4. What is the main purpose of a specification?
5. What is the purpose of the bill of quantities?
6. What is a penalty clause?
7. What does the approved document A cover?
8. Which approved document deals with stairs?
9. What is the role of the Building Inspector?

chapter 3

Planning and work programmes

OVERVIEW

Any building project begins long before the first brick is laid or the first foundation dug. Most buildings and construction projects will need some sort of planning approval before they get underway, as a range of planning restrictions are in place to keep building standards up, protect local people and protect the environment.

Work planning is also of paramount importance for every job, whether a single dwelling or a large housing estate. Without it even the smallest job can go wrong: something simple is forgotten or omitted, such as ordering a skip, and the job is suddenly delayed by anything up to a week. On a smaller job, poor planning can result in delays, which will harm your reputation and jeopardise future contracts. With larger contracts, penalty clauses can be costly: if the job overruns and isn't finished on time, the client may claim substantial amounts of money from the contractor. This chapter will deal with:

- external planning restrictions
- work programming.

External planning restrictions

Before starting to plan a building project, it is important to know how your plans may be affected by local and national building restrictions. The two main sets of restrictions you will come across are:

- the Building Regulations
- planning permission.

It is crucial that anyone planning a construction project understands how these work, and seeks the necessary approval in the correct way. If not, building work runs the risk of having to be halted, altered or even taken down.

The Building Regulations

The Building Regulations were first introduced in the late 1800s to improve the appalling housing conditions common then. The Public Health Act 1875 allowed local authorities to make their own laws regarding the planning and construction of buildings. There were many grey areas and **inconsistencies** between local authorities, especially where one authority bordered another.

Building Regulations help protect the environment

This system remained in place for almost a century until the Building Regulations 1965 came into force. These replaced all local laws with a uniform Act for all in England and Wales to follow. The only exception was inner London, which was covered by the London Building Acts. The Government passed a new law in 1984, setting up the Building Regulations 1985 to cover all England and Wales, including inner London.

The current law is the Building Regulations 2000, amended in April 2006 to take into account things such as wheelchair access and more environmentally friendly practices. The current law also covers all England and Wales.

Scotland is governed slightly differently and is covered by the Building (Scotland) Act 2003. Northern Ireland is covered by the Building (Amendment) Regulations (Northern Ireland) 2006 which came into effect in November 2006.

The main purpose of the Building Regulations is to ensure the health, safety and welfare of all people in and around buildings as well as to further energy conservation and to protect the environment. The regulations apply to most new buildings as well as any alterations to existing buildings, whether they are domestic, commercial or industrial. Many projects also require planning permission, which is covered on pages 43–45.

These are the types of work classified as needing Building Regulations approval:

- the erection of an extension or building
- the installation or extension of a service or fitting which is controlled under the regulations
- an alteration project involving work which will temporarily or permanently affect the ongoing compliance of the building, service, or fitting with the requirements relating to structure, fire, or access to and the use of the building
- the insertion of insulation into a cavity wall
- the underpinning of the foundations of a building
- work affecting the thermal elements, energy status or energy performance of the building.

If you are unsure whether the work you are going to carry out needs Building Regulations approval, contact the local authority.

The Building Regulations are enforced by two types of building control bodies: local authority building control and Approved Inspector building control. If you wish to apply for approval, you must contact one of these bodies.

If you use an Approved Inspector, you must contact the local authority to tell them what is being done where, stating that the Inspector will be responsible for the control of the work.

The Building Inspector will need to be involved at every key stage

If you choose to go to the local authority, there are three ways of applying for consent:

- **full plans** – Plans are submitted to the local authority along with any specifications and other contract documents. The local authority scrutinises these and makes a decision.
- **building notice** – A less detailed amount of information is submitted (but more can be requested) and no decision is made. The approval process is determined by the stage the work is at.
- **regularisation** – This is a means of applying for approval for work that has already been completed without approval.

The Building Inspector will make regular visits to ensure that the work is being carried out to the standards set down in the application, and that no extra unapproved work is being done. Often the contractor will tell the Inspector when the job has reached a certain stage, so that they can come in and check what has been done. If the Inspector is not informed at key stages, he/she can ask for the work to be opened up to be checked.

Building Regulations approval is not always given but there is an appeals procedure. For more information, contact your local authority.

Planning permission

As has already been mentioned, with most contracts you must have planning permission as well as Building Regulations approval before starting the work.

Planning permission laws were introduced to stop people building whatever they like wherever they like. The submission of a planning application gives both the local authority and the general public a chance to look at the development, to see if it is in keeping with the local area and whether it serves the interests of the local community.

The main **remit** of planning laws is to control the use and development of land in order to obtain the greatest possible environmental advantages with the least inconvenience for both the person/s applying for permission and society as a whole.

The key word in planning is 'development', defined in planning law as 'the carrying out of building, engineering, mining or other operations in, on, over or under land, or the making of any material change in the use of any buildings or other land'. As well as building work, this covers the construction of a new road or driveway, and even change of use: if a bank is to be turned into a wine bar, planning permission will be needed.

Planning permission is required for most forms of development. Here are a few more examples of work requiring planning permission:

- virtually all new building work
- house extensions including conservatories, loft conversions and roof additions (such as dormers)
- buildings and other structures on the land including garages
- adding a porch to your house
- putting up a TV satellite dish.

Did you know?

Planning permission is needed if you want to put up a satellite dish. The job itself is small and not disruptive, but a dish is thought to change the outer appearance of a house enough to need permission

The public has a right to know about proposed developments

Even if you are intending to work from home and wish to convert part of your home into an office, you will require planning permission if:

- your home is no longer to be used mainly as a private residence
- your business creates more traffic or creates problems with parking due to people calling
- your business involves any activities classed as unusual in a **residential** area
- Your business disturbs your neighbours at unreasonable hours or creates other forms of nuisance or smell.

Not all work requires planning. You can make certain types of minor alterations to your house, such as putting up a fence or dividing wall (providing it is less than 1 metre high next to a highway, or under 2 metres elsewhere), without planning permission.

In areas such as conservation areas or classified Areas of Outstanding Natural Beauty there will be stricter controls on what is allowed. Listed buildings also have stricter controls and come under the Planning (Listed Buildings and Conservation Areas) Act 1990.

For planning permission, you must apply to your local council. When they look at your proposed works, they will take into consideration:

- the number, size, positioning, layout and external appearance of the buildings
- the proposed means of access, landscaping and impact on the neighbourhood
- **sustainability**, and whether the necessary infrastructure, such as roads, services, etc., will be available
- the proposed use of the development.

Several steps are involved in applying for planning permission. The first is to contact the local council to see if they think planning permission is required (some councils may charge a small fee for this advice). If they say you do need planning permission, you need to then ask them for an application form. There are two types of planning permission that you can apply for:

- **outline application** This can be made if you want to see what the council thinks of the building work you intend to do before you go to the trouble of having costly plans drawn up. Details of the work will have to be submitted later if the outline application is successful.
- **full application** Here a full application is made with all the plans, specifications, and so on.

Once you have completed the relevant form this must be sent to the council along with any fee.

Next, the contents of your application will be publicised so that people can express their views and raise any objections. A copy will be placed in the planning register; an electronic version will be placed on the council's website; and immediate neighbours will be written to (or a fixed

Find out

Look online for your local authority's website. Most now have the main information you need for planning matters, and you may even be able to download the forms you need to use notice will be displayed on or as near as possible to the site). The council may also advertise your application in a local newspaper. As the applicant, you will be entitled to have a copy of any reports, objections and expressions of support the council receives regarding your application.

The council normally takes up to eight weeks to make a decision on your application but in some cases it may take longer. If this happens, the council should write asking for your written consent to extend the period. If your application is not dealt with within eight weeks, you can appeal to the Secretary of State, but this can be a lengthy procedure itself, so it is best to try to resolve the matter at a local level.

In looking at an application, the council considers whether there are valid reasons for refusing or granting permission: the council cannot simply reject a proposal because many people oppose it. The council will look at whether your proposal is consistent with the area's appearance, whether it will cause traffic problems and whether it has any impact on local amenities, environment and services.

Once an application has been looked at, there are four possible outcomes: permission refused; application still pending; granted with conditions; or granted.

- **Permission refused**

  If permission is refused, the council must state its reasons for turning down the application. If you feel these are unfair, you can appeal to the Secretary of State. Appeals must be made within six months of the council's decision and are intended as a last resort. It can take months to get a decision, which may be a refusal. Alternatively, you can ask what changes need to be made to allow the proposal to pass: if these are acceptable, the amended application can be submitted for processing. If after this the application is still rejected, the work cannot go ahead. However, different authorities have different procedures, so always check before submitting proposals.

- **Application still pending**

  Here the council may have found that it needs extra time to allow comments to come in, or to deal with particular issues that have arisen. If the application is still pending then, as stated previously, the council must ask for your written consent to extend the period for making a decision.

- **Granted with conditions**

  In this case you are able to start the work, remembering to comply with the conditions stated. If you fail to comply, permission will be revoked and you may be ordered to undo the work done. If you are unhappy with the conditions set, you can ask for advice and, if needs be, make alterations to the plans. This would mean resubmitting the application.

- **Granted**

  If you have been granted permission, you are free to start the work.

Remember

If you build something without planning permission then you may be forced to **dismantle** the building and put it back to the original state – as well as paying for the work yourself!

Work programming

Once planning permission and Building Regulations approval have been obtained, the next step is to plan the work (NB in some instances the client may ask the contractor to provide a work programme at the tender stage, to check the contractor's efficiency and organising ability).

A work programme is vital for good work planning, as it shows:

- what tasks are to be done and when, including any overlap in the tasks
- what materials are required and when
- what plant is needed, when and for how long
- what type of workforce is required and when.

A few different types of work programme are in use, and we will cover the main two on pages 48–52.

Planning the site

Remember

If you need to plan several sites, save the cut-outs from one to use on the next (checking that you are using the same scale). You could end up with a 'kit' to use whenever you need it.

For every fair-sized job, the building site needs to be carefully planned. A poorly planned site can cause problems and delays, as well as incurring costs and even causing accidents.

A building site should be seen as a temporary workshop, store and office for the contractor, and must contain all the **amenities** needed on a permanent base. Sites should be planned in a way that minimises the movement of employees, materials and plant throughout the construction, while at the same time providing protection and security for employees, materials and components, and members of the public. A well-planned site will also have good transport routes, which will not disrupt the site or the general traffic.

Many things need to be included on a building site, so it is often easiest to plan your site using a site plan and cut-outs of the amenities you need. These cut-outs can be laid onto the plan and moved around until a suitable layout is found.

The ideal layout of the site will vary according to the size and **duration** of the job – there is no point hiring site offices for a job that will only last a day! The following gives an idea of what might be needed on an average site:

- **site offices**

  The office space (usually portable cabins) should be of a decent size, usually with more than one room for different members of staff and a large room for meetings. Phone, fax and email facilities will be needed, so that the site office can communicate with Head Office, contractors, suppliers and others. As with any office, the site office must be heated, have plenty of light (natural or artificial) and be fitted out with useful, comfortable furniture.

- **first aid office**

  This is sometimes contained within the site office, but on larger sites a separate space may be needed so that injured people can be treated quickly and efficiently. The first aid office must be fully stocked, and there must be sufficient trained first aiders on site.

- **toilets**

  There must be sufficient toilets on the site. Usually there will be a WC block next to the canteen or mess area, with additional portable toilets dotted around the site if needed. Toilets must be kept clean and well stocked at all times, and have somewhere for people to wash their hands. The WC block may also need to house showers if the work being done requires them.

- **lunch area**

  This should be protected from the wind and rain and have heating and electricity. It should contain equipment such as a microwave, kettle or urn and fridge to heat and keep food, as well as suitable food storage such as cupboards. There should be adequate seating and tables, and the space should be kept clean to prevent any unwelcome pests such as rats or cockroaches.

- **drying room**

  This provides space for employees to dry off any clothes that get wet, on the way to or during work. It is usually sited next to the lunch area, or is part of the same building. The room must have adequate heating and ventilation, as well as lockers or storage to house things like motorcycle helmets.

- **cranes, hoists, etc.**

  These can be static or portable. When a large static crane is required, its position needs to be planned so that it can easily and safely reach the area where it is needed. Larger cranes should be situated away from the main site office for safety reasons.

- **transport route**

  Having a good transport route into, out of and within a building site is vital. It is best to have separate entrances and exits, with a one-way system on the site and good signposting throughout. These measures will avoid large delivery lorries having to turn around on site, and help to keep both internal and external traffic flowing with minimum disruption.

- **waste area**

  This must be well away from the lunch area for health and safety reasons, and should be easily accessible from the transport route so that the skips and bins can be emptied easily. Separate well-labelled skips are needed for different kinds of refuse, and there should be some for recycling. Certain skips should be kept separate to avoid **contamination**, and chemical dumps (for paint, etc.) should be kept secure and emptied regularly.

Various types of storage are also needed on a building site, such as:

- **materials storage** – enough adequate space to store all types of materials, ideally near to where they are being used (for example, cement and sand should be stored near the mixer). All materials should be stored in a way that prevents them being damaged or stolen; some materials will have to be stored separately to avoid contamination.
- **component storage** – a secure compound protected from the wind and rain for items such as doors and windows. Again, components should be stored in a way that prevents them being damaged.
- **tool storage** – a secure place for employees' own tools as well as site tools such as table saws. The tool storage area needs to be thoroughly secure to prevent theft.
- **ironmongery storage** – a locked compound in a container with well-labelled racks to avoid things like screws and nails being mixed up. Expensive ironmongery such as door furniture needs to be properly secure. On a well-planned site, expensive ironmongery is only ordered when needed.

A good site layout might look something like this.

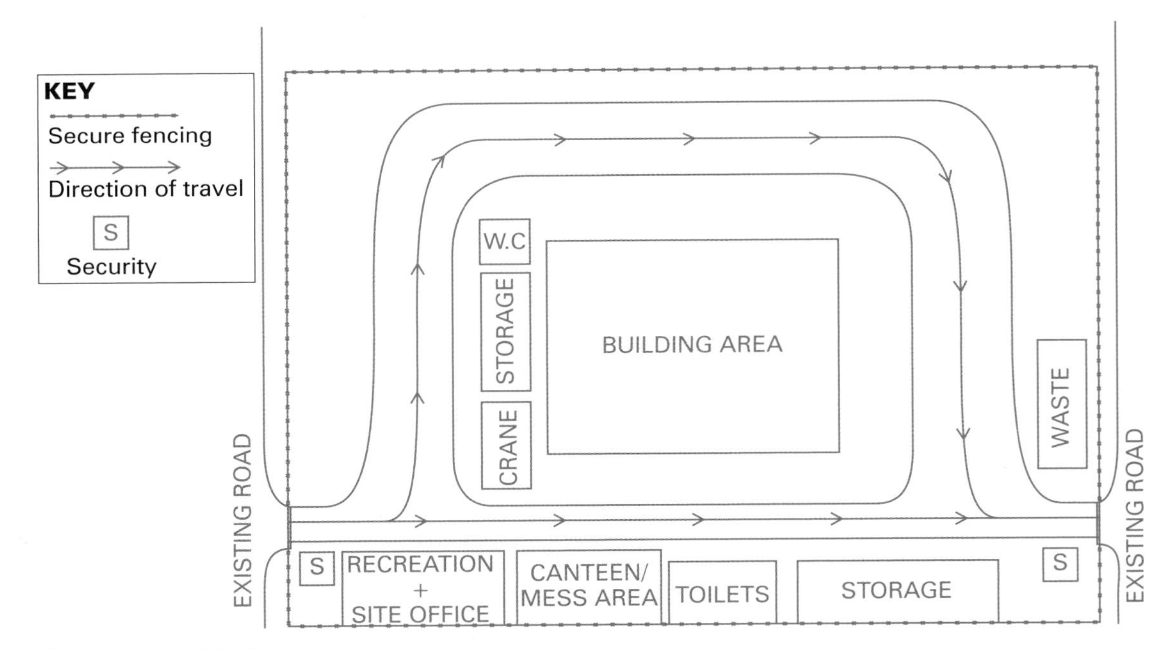

Figure 3.1 Good site layout

Planning the work

There are many types of work programme, including the critical path and the Bar/Gantt chart. The latter is the one you will come across most often.

Bar charts

The bar or Gantt chart is the most popular work programme as it is simple to construct and easy to understand. Bar charts have tasks listed in a vertical column on the left and a horizontal timescale running along the top.

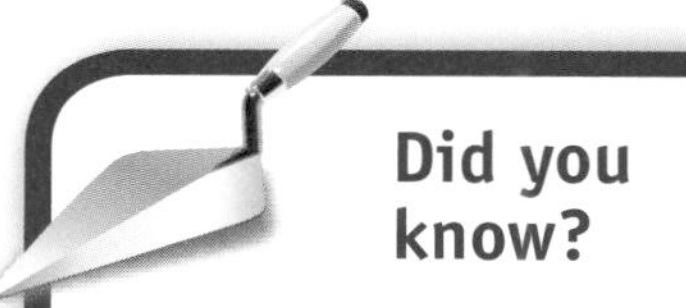

The Gantt chart is named after the first man to publish it. This was Henry Gantt, an American engineer, in 1910.

	Time in days									
Activity	1	2	3	4	5	6	7	8	9	10
Dig for foundation and service routes										
Lay foundations										
Run cabling, piping etc. to meet existing services										
Build up to DPC										
Lay concrete floor										

Figure 3.2 Basic bar chart

Each task is given a proposed time, which is shaded in along the horizontal timescale. Timescales often overlap as one task often overlaps another.

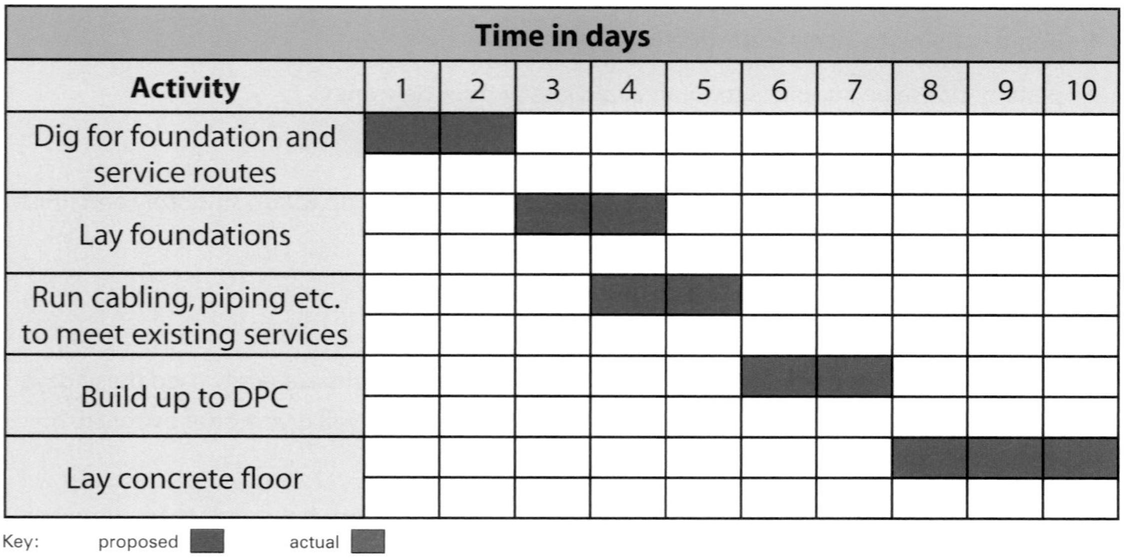

	Time in days									
Activity	1	2	3	4	5	6	7	8	9	10
Dig for foundation and service routes	■	■								
Lay foundations			■	■						
Run cabling, piping etc. to meet existing services				■	■					
Build up to DPC						■	■			
Lay concrete floor								■	■	■

Key: proposed ■ actual ■

Figure 3.3 Bar chart showing proposed time for a contract

The bar chart can then be used to check progress. Often the actual time taken for a task is shaded in underneath the proposed time (in a different way or colour to avoid confusion). This shows how what *has* been done matches up to what *should have* been done.

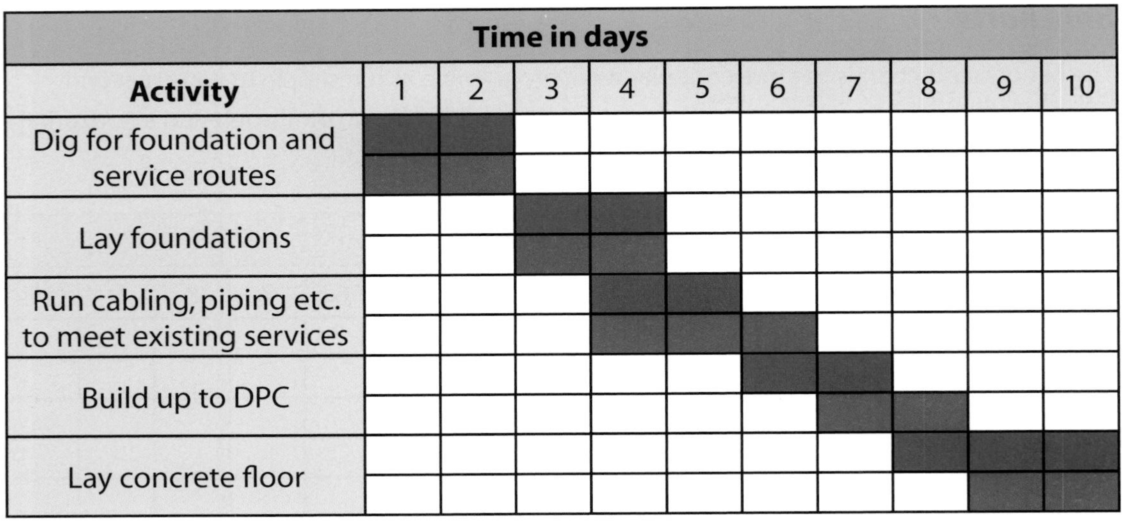

Activity	Time in days									
	1	2	3	4	5	6	7	8	9	10
Dig for foundation and service routes										
Lay foundations										
Run cabling, piping etc. to meet existing services										
Build up to DPC										
Lay concrete floor										

Figure 3.4 Bar chart showing actual time half way through a contract Key: proposed actual

As you can see, a bar chart can help you plan when to order materials or plant, see what trade is due in and when, and so on. A bar chart can also tell you if you are behind on a job; if you have a penalty clause written into your contract, this information is vital.

When creating a bar chart, you should build in some extra time to allow for things such as bad weather, labour shortages, delivery problems or illness. It is also advisable to have contingency plans to help solve or avoid problems, such as:

- capacity to work overtime to catch up time
- bonus scheme to increase productivity
- penalty clause on suppliers to try to avoid late or poor deliveries
- source of extra labour (e.g. from another site) if needed.

Good planning, with contingency plans in place, should allow a job to run smoothly and finish on time, leading to the contractor making a profit.

Did you know?

Bad weather is the main external factor responsible for delays on building sites in the UK. A Met Office survey showed that the average UK construction company experiences problems caused by the weather 26 times a year

Critical paths

Another form of work programme is the critical path. Critical paths are rarely used these days as they can be difficult to decipher. The final part of this chapter will give a brief overview of the basics of a critical path, in case you should come across one.

A critical path can be used in the same way as a bar chart to show what needs to be done and in what sequence. It also shows a timescale but in a different way to a bar chart: each timescale shows both the minimum and the maximum amount of time a task might take.

The critical path is shown as a series of circles called event nodes. Each node is split into three: the top third shows the event number, the bottom left shows the earliest start time, and the bottom right the latest start time.

The nodes are joined together by lines, which represent the tasks being carried out between those nodes. The length of each task is shown by the times written in the lower parts of the nodes. Some critical paths have information on each task written underneath the lines that join the nodes, making them easier to read.

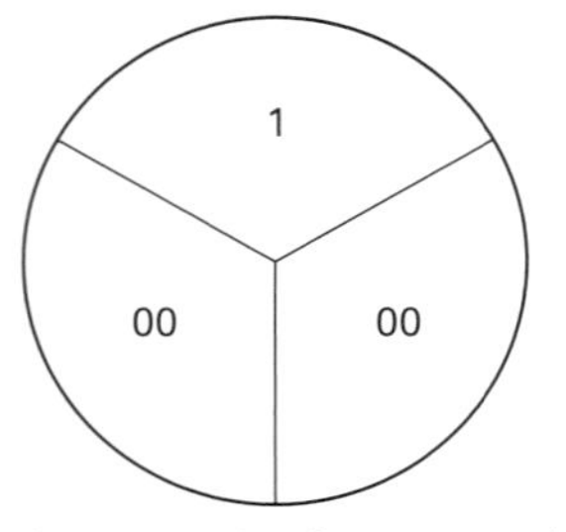

Figure 3.5 Single event node

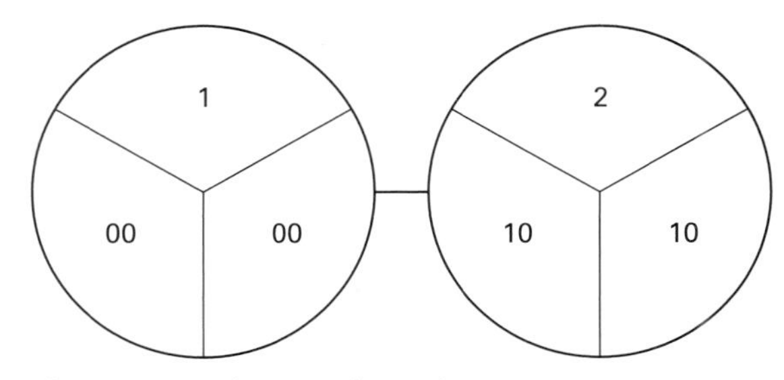

Figure 3.6 Nodes joined together

On a job, many tasks can be worked on at the same time, e.g. the electricians may be wiring at the same time as the plumber putting in his pipes. To show this on a critical path, the path can be split.

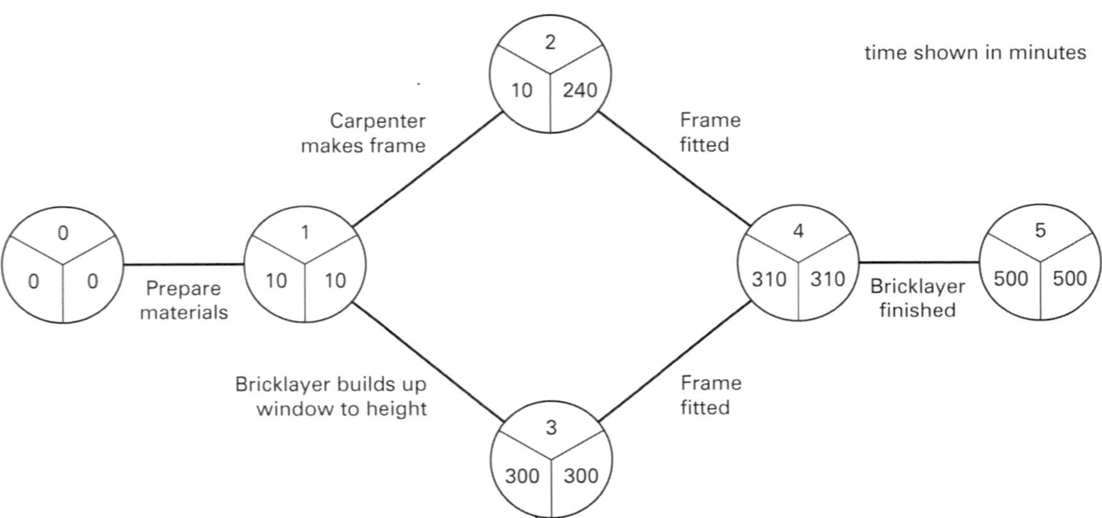

Figure 3.7 Split path

The example shown shows how a critical path can be used for planning building in a window opening, with a carpenter creating a dummy frame.

The event nodes work as follows:

- **Node 0 –** This is the starting point.
- **Node 1 –** This is the first task, where the materials are prepared.
- **Node 2 –** This is where the carpenter makes the dummy frame for the opening. Notice that the earliest start time is 10 minutes and the last start time is 240 minutes. This means that the carpenter can start building the frame at any time between 10 minutes and 240 minutes into the project. This is because the frame will not be needed until 300 minutes, but the job will only take 60 minutes. If the carpenter starts *after* 240 minutes, there is a possibility that the job may run behind.
- **Node 3 –** This is where the bricklayer must be at the site, ready for the frame to be fitted at 300 minutes, or the job will run behind.

- **Node 4 –** With the frame fitted, the bricklayer starts at 310 minutes and has until node 5 (500 minutes) to finish.
- **Node 5 –** The job should be completed.

Remember

Whichever way you choose to programme your work, your programme must be realistic, with clear objectives and achievable goals

When working with a split path it is vital to remember that certain tasks have to be completed before others can begin. If this is not taken into account on the critical path, the job will run over (which may prove costly, both through penalty clauses and also in terms of the contractor's reputation).

On a large job, it can be easy to misread a critical path as there may be several splits, which could lead to confusion.

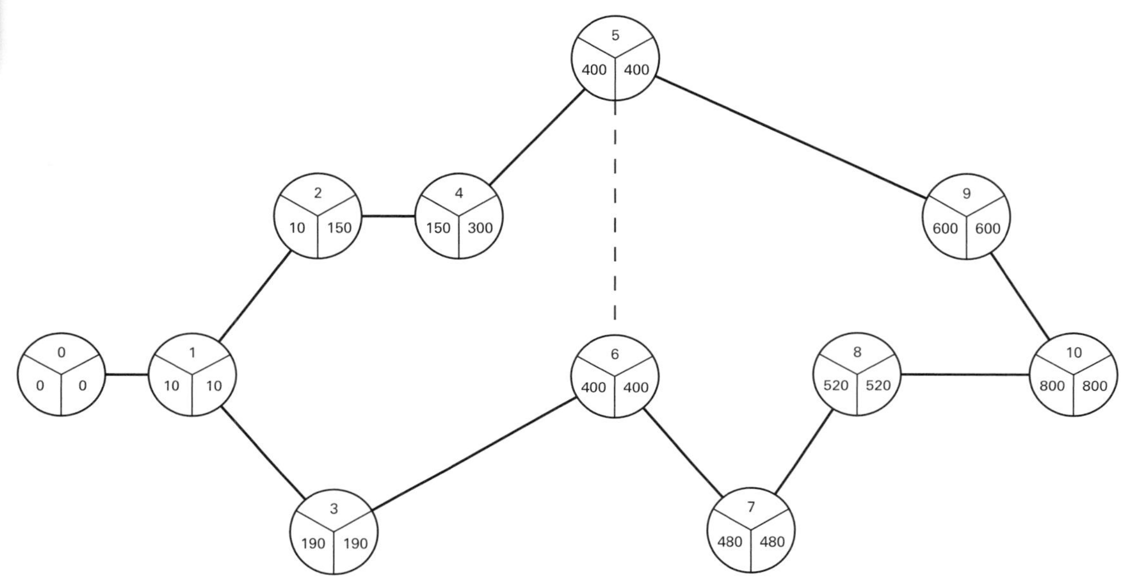

Figure 3.8 Critical path for a large job

On the job: Planning a site

Sanjit is planning a site. When he sets out what is needed with regards to toilets, lunch areas and so on, he opts to use the same entrance and exit for site transport. What problems can this cause, both on and off site?

FAQ

How do I know if my job needs planning permission?

If you are unsure, you should contact your local council.

What type of planning permission should I apply for?

If you are unsure of your work, you can make an outline application, which will tell you if your job will pass without getting costly plans made up (though you will have to submit plans later). If you are confident of what you want, you can apply for a full application.

How much does planning permission cost?

The costs vary depending on what application you make and to which council you make it.

Do I need to have all the listed amenities on my building site?

No. The amenities listed are a guide to what should be on a large site. If you are just doing an extension, the amenities needed will be fewer and simpler (e.g. no site office).

Which type of programme should I use: bar chart or critical path?

It is up to the individual which programme they use – both have their good points – but a bar chart is the easiest to set up and work from.

Knowledge check

1. When were the first Building Regulations covering all England and Wales introduced?
2. Why were planning laws introduced?
3. What do planning laws define as 'development'?
4. If you plan to use your home as an office, what changes require planning permission?
5. State the two types of planning you can apply for.
6. What are the four possible outcomes from the council regarding a planning application?
7. List four things that might be included in the layout for a large site.
8. State four pieces of information you can get from a bar chart.
9. What is the purpose of a contingency plan?
10. With regard to critical paths, what three things are contained in an event node?

chapter 4

The building process

OVERVIEW

The building process covers the construction of a building from start to finish. In this chapter we will look at what and who is involved at every step. We will follow a fictitious job through all stages of the building process showing what documents are used when, as well as who is responsible for carrying out the work and when.

This chapter is meant as a guide only. In some circumstances, or in certain areas of the country, the process may differ slightly. The documents used in our example may not all be needed for every job, but an awareness of each document is very important.

The information is broken down into several sections for easy reference, as follows:

- who's who
- getting started
- contract documents
- specification
- bill of quantities
- Building Regulations and planning permission
- work programming
- site set-up
- starting the work
- completing the work.

Who's who

Many different people are involved in the process of building, and together they are known as the building team. For a full rundown of members of the building team, you can refer to *Brickwork NVQ and Technical Certificate Level 2* pages 6–9, but here is a brief description of the main players:

Client – every single job starts with the client, the most important person. Without the client, there is no job.

Architect – works closely with the client and produces contract documents such as the plans and specification.

Local authority – is responsible for checking whether the construction meets all planning and Building Regulations.

Health and Safety Inspectors – are employed by the Health and Safety Executive to ensure that all building work is done in line with health and safety regulations.

Quantity surveyor – works with the architect and client to produce the bill of quantities, which is sent to contractors to enable them to submit tenders.

Contractor – works for the client and carries out the building work in line with the plans.

Sub-contractor – is employed by the contractor to carry out specialist work that the contractor cannot do themselves.

Site agent – is responsible for the day-to-day running of the site, including monitoring the programme of work.

Foreman – works under the site agent and is responsible for organising the work of the craft operatives and sub-contractors.

Operatives – the people, skilled or semi-skilled, who actually carry out the work.

Remember

Health and safety during the course of a contract is paramount and health and safety legislation applies all the way through the contract, from start to finish. Throughout this chapter we will remind you of what health and safety documents, contacts or actions need to be completed

Getting started

Every building contract begins with a client who needs work done, whether it is an extension or a whole scheme of houses. The example we will use in this chapter is the building of a garage with an upstairs office. There are normally two ways the client can proceed:

1. The client contacts contractors who will come out, have a look at the job and price it up. The client picks the contractor and agrees the price, then the contractor does the work. With this method only some of the contract documents are used. The client will be left to apply for planning and Building Regulations approval without the aid of an architect.

2. The client contacts an architect to discuss the work and from then on the architect takes control, acting as the client's representative. With this method, all of the contract documents (including the bill of quantities) are used, and the job's progress is recorded on a programme.

It is possible to mix the two methods, but generally method 1 is used on small jobs such as extensions or loft conversions while method 2 is used for larger jobs such as new housing estates or supermarkets. Method 2 is more expensive as it uses more members of the building team, but this approach ensures a properly planned job.

Please note: method 1 would be the one normally used for our example (the building of a garage with an upstairs office) but for the purposes of this book and to show you more of the building process we will imagine that the client has chosen to use method 2.

First the client contacts an architect and arranges a meeting, at which the client tells the architect their wishes. The architect then does rough sketches of what the client wants and prepares a rough specification. If the client is happy with the architect's work, he/she will give the architect the go ahead to prepare full contract documents.

Contract documents

The architect starts with the plans, doing several different plans including block plans, site plans, general location drawings and detailed drawings (examples of all of these can be found in Chapter 2, pages 18–22). Below are the types of the drawings that would be required, to give you an idea of the job and what it entails. Full architects' drawings would give more information, such as the positioning of services.

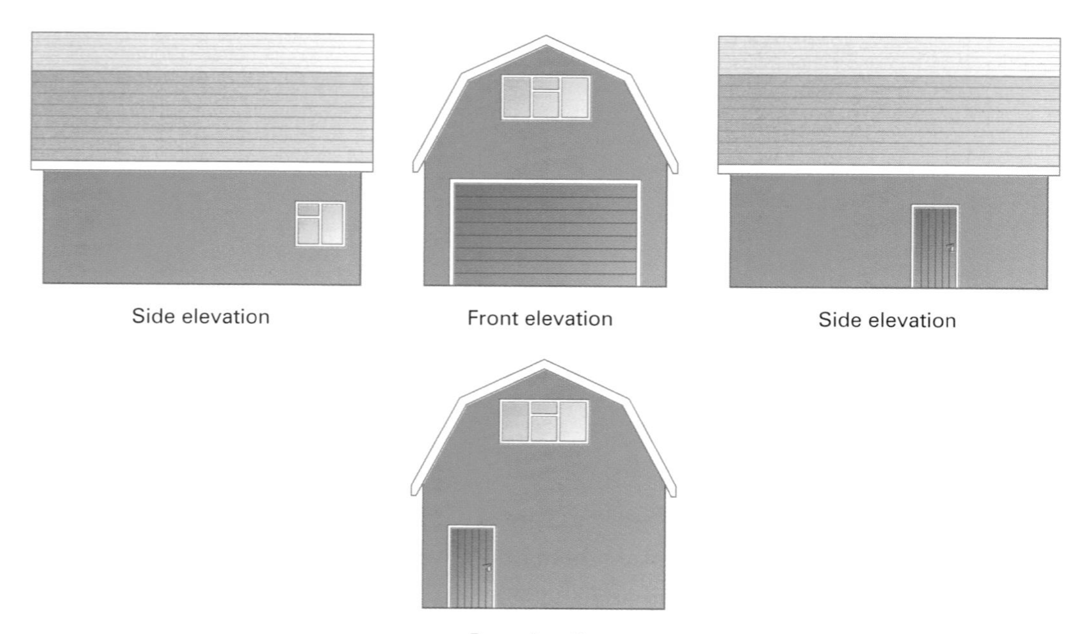

Figure 4.1 Elevation drawings

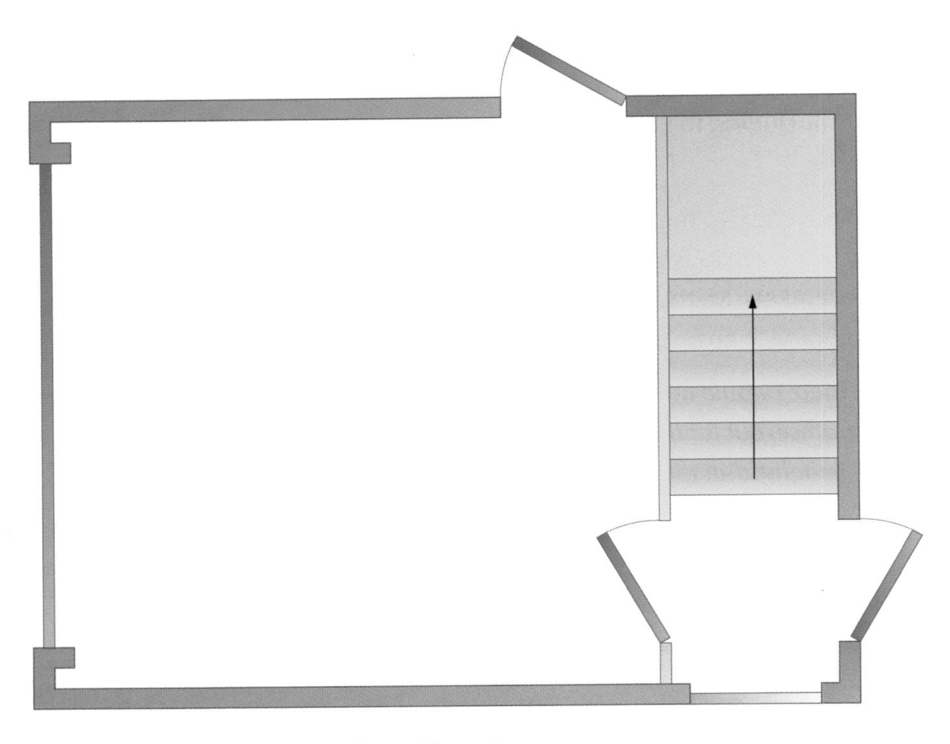

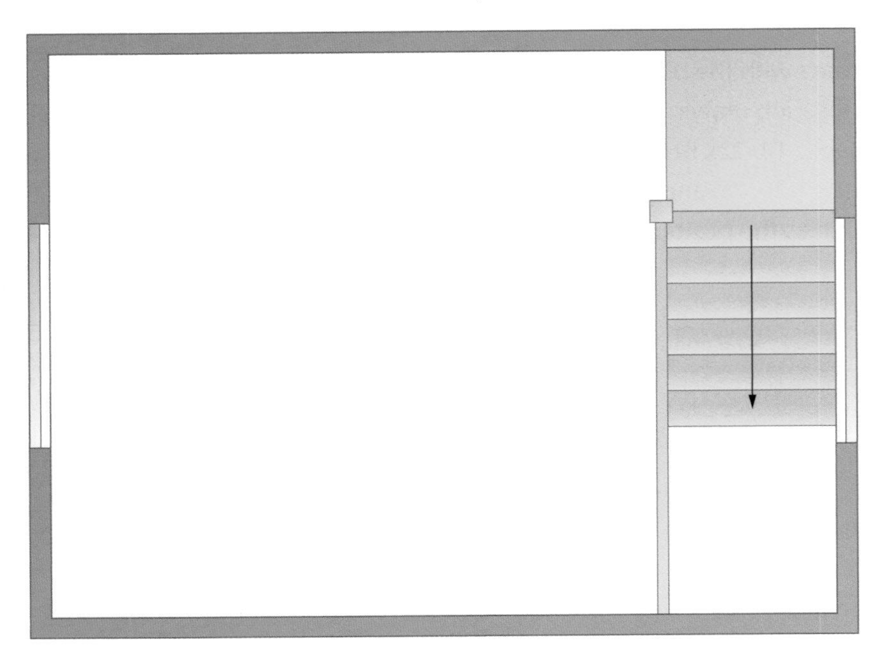

Figure 4.2 Floor plans

Once all the drawings are completed and the client is happy with them, the architect then draws up a specification and, if needed, a schedule. A schedule is not required for this project but an example schedule can be found on page 25.

Specification

The specification is next. This is used alongside the main drawings and gives information that cannot be worked out from the drawings. A full specification for even a small job like this can run to several pages, so what you see below is only a brief extract, covering the workmanship and materials used for constructing the upper floor.

Joists – 47 × 220mm pre-cut, pressure **impregnated**, structurally graded joists @ max. 400mm centres. Joists must be **regularised** and laid with the rounds facing up

Joist hangers – galvanised steel joist hangers built into brickwork with associated fixings for securing joists in place

Insulation – 100mm foil-backed, rigid insulation and 100mm high density (24 kg/m^3) Rockwool insulation fitted between joists + 400mm wide strip of 100mm insulation around perimeter

Flooring – 22mm tongued and grooved, moisture resistant flooring grade chipboard (V313 – TG4). Flooring to be glued at every joint and screwed @ no less than 8" centres

Solid blocking, noggins and herringbone strutting, as appropriate

Figure 4.3 Flooring specification

Definition

Regularised joists – joists run through a saw to ensure that they are all the same depth, which will ensure a flat, even ceiling and floor

The next two sections are very closely tied together. Either can be done first but to save time it is ideal to do both at the same time.

Bill of quantities

The quantity surveyor uses all the contract documents from the architect to help draw up the bill of quantities.

Again, even for such a small job the bill of quantities can run to several pages, so for our example we will look at a bill of quantities for just the upper floor part of the contract.

Item ref no	Description	Quantity	Unit	Rate £	Cost £
UF 1	47 × 220mm pre-cut, pressure impregnated, structurally graded joists	180	M	2.79	502.20
UF 2	50mm galvanised steel joist hangers	54	N/A	1.00	54.00
UF 3	100mm foil-backed, rigid insulation	10	N/A	22.78	227.80
UF 4	100mm high density (24kg/m³) Rockwool insulation	10	N/A	15.68	156.80
UF 5	22mm tongued and grooved, moisture resistant flooring grade chipboard (V313 – TG4)	50	N/A	5.46	273.00
UF 6	Fixings and adhesives	N/A	N/A	50.00	50.00
UF 7	Labour to fit the above to the required specification	64	N/A	15.00	960.00
			Total		2223.80

Figure 4.4 Bill of quantities

Building Regulations and planning permission

The contract documents are sent to the local council for planning permission approval, which could take up to eight weeks to come through. The plans are also sent to the local authority for Building Regulations approval. At this stage it can be helpful to contact the local Health and Safety Executive outlining what is being done. This gives them the opportunity to raise any immediate concerns they may have with the contract or to give any advice. It is also advisable to complete a F10 form for the Health and Safety Executive, informing them that construction work is about to take place. The F10 is only needed if the contract will last longer than 30 calendar days or 500 people days.

Definition

People days – a way of expressing how long it will take to do something, by looking at how many people will be needed for how long. For example, if you need four people, each working for two days, your total number of people days is 4 x 2 = 8

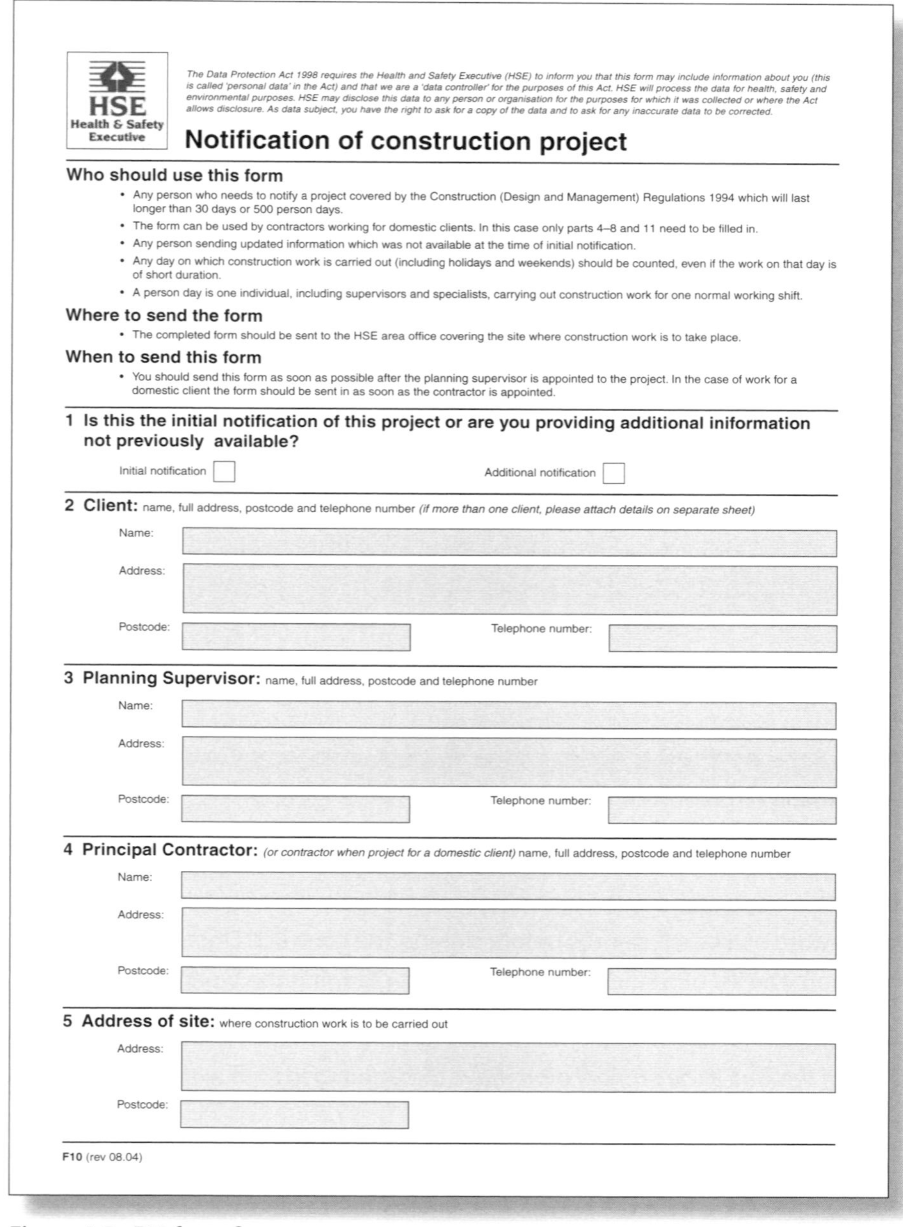

HSE Health & Safety Executive

The Data Protection Act 1998 requires the Health and Safety Executive (HSE) to inform you that this form may include information about you (this is called 'personal data' in the Act) and that we are a 'data controller' for the purposes of this Act. HSE will process the data for health, safety and environmental purposes. HSE may disclose this data to any person or organisation for the purposes for which it was collected or where the Act allows disclosure. As data subject, you have the right to ask for a copy of the data and to ask for any inaccurate data to be corrected.

Notification of construction project

Who should use this form
- Any person who needs to notify a project covered by the Construction (Design and Management) Regulations 1994 which will last longer than 30 days or 500 person days.
- The form can be used by contractors working for domestic clients. In this case only parts 4–8 and 11 need to be filled in.
- Any person sending updated information which was not available at the time of initial notification.
- Any day on which construction work is carried out (including holidays and weekends) should be counted, even if the work on that day is of short duration.
- A person day is one individual, including supervisors and specialists, carrying out construction work for one normal working shift.

Where to send the form
- The completed form should be sent to the HSE area office covering the site where construction work is to take place.

When to send this form
- You should send this form as soon as possible after the planning supervisor is appointed to the project. In the case of work for a domestic client the form should be sent in as soon as the contractor is appointed.

1 Is this the initial notification of this project or are you providing additional information not previously available?

Initial notification ☐ Additional notification ☐

2 Client: name, full address, postcode and telephone number *(if more than one client, please attach details on separate sheet)*

Name:

Address:

Postcode: Telephone number:

3 Planning Supervisor: name, full address, postcode and telephone number

Name:

Address:

Postcode: Telephone number:

4 Principal Contractor: *(or contractor when project for a domestic client)* name, full address, postcode and telephone number

Name:

Address:

Postcode: Telephone number:

5 Address of site: where construction work is to be carried out

Address:

Postcode:

F10 (rev 08.04)

Figure 4.5a F10 form, first page

Did you know?

The cheapest tender is not always the one that wins the contract. Some contractors include in their tender bids that they will recycle so much waste, or employ so many people from the local workforce. Things like this can be the deciding factors in winning a contract

6 Local Authority:
Name of the local government council or authority within whose area the construction work is to be carried out.

7 Please give your estimates on the following:
Please indicate if these estimates are: original ☐ revised ☐ *(tick relevant box)*

a. The planned date for the commencement of the construction work

b. How long the construction work is expected to take *(in weeks)*

c. The maximum number of people carrying out construction work on site at any one time

d. The number of contractors expected to work on site

8 Construction work: give brief details of the type of construction work that will be carried out

9 Contractors: name, full address and postcode of those who have been chosen to work on this project *(if required continue on a separate sheet). (Note this information is only required when it is known at the time notification is first made to HSE. An update is not required)*

10 Declaration of planning supervisor

I hereby declare that *(name of organisation)* has been appointed as planning supervisor for the project

Signed by or on behalf of the organisation

Print name

Date

11 Declaration of principal contractor

I hereby declare that *(name of principal contractor)* has been appointed as principal contractor for the project

Signed by or on behalf of the organisation

Print name

Date

Figure 4.5b F10 form, second page

Once the planning permission and Building Regulations approvals are received, it is time to select a contractor. At this stage any clauses such as penalty clauses are introduced – the contractor must be made aware of all such clauses before signing the contract. Once the contractor has been selected from the list of tenders, it is time to start planning the work programme.

The next two sections should also be done at the same time. To save time they can sometimes be done earlier than this but, if the original plans have to be changed to fit with Building Regulations or planning permission, this may prove costly.

Work programming

The bar chart for our example looks something like this:

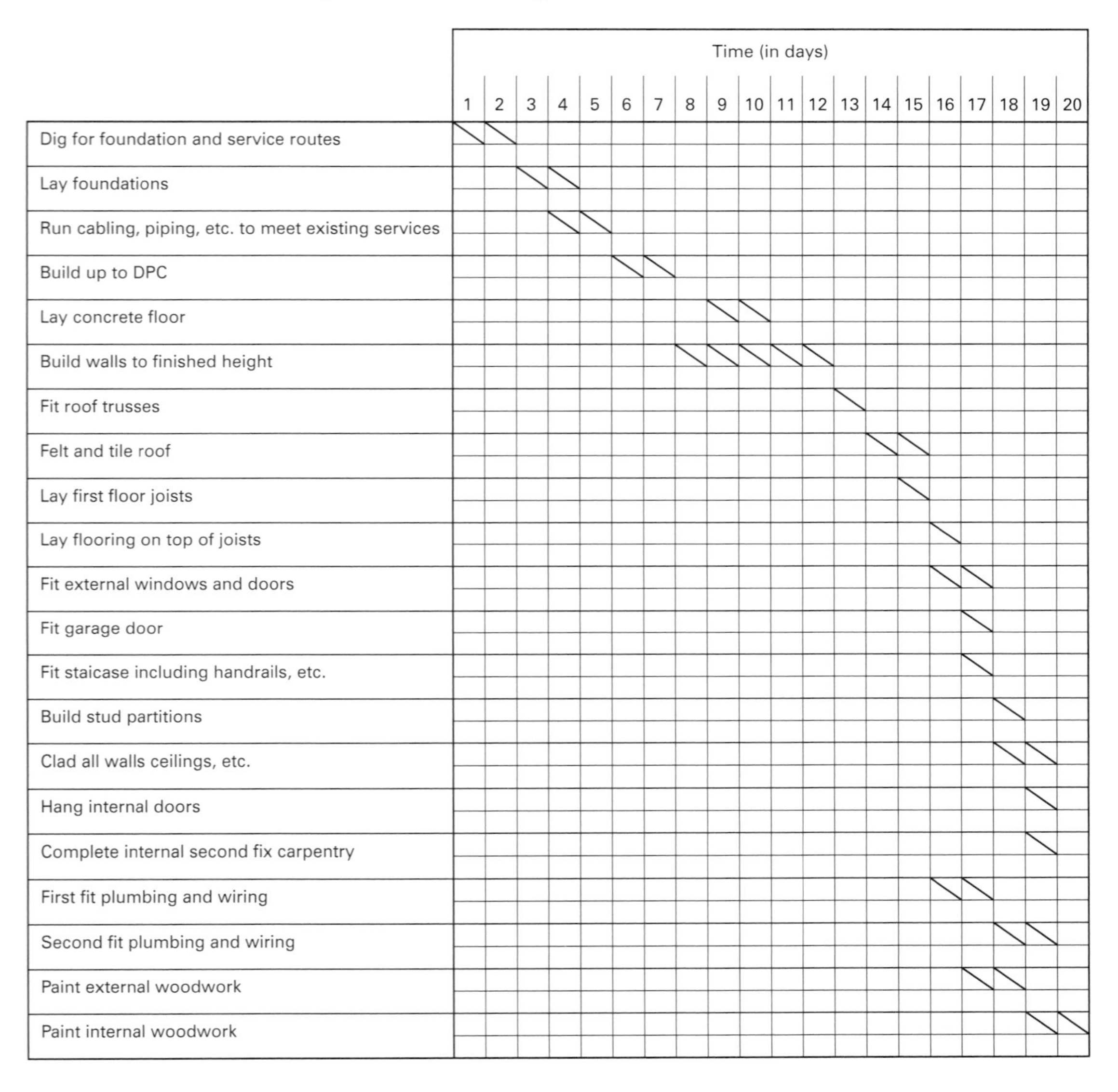

Figure 4.6 Work programme

As you can see the work programme is divided into two with the 'proposed' section completed. The 'actual' section will be completed as the job progresses.

Once the programme has been set up and start dates have been confirmed, it is time for the contractor to contact suppliers, sub-contractors, etc., and to order materials, labour and plant.

You can see from the programme that the first task is to get the foundations done, so it is vital that all the relevant plant, labour and materials are on site ready to start on the required date. Carpenters do not need to be on site yet, but it is good practice to ensure in advance that they will be available to start work on the required dates.

It is bad practice to order all the materials this early (having items like doors delivered to site at this stage could lead to them being damaged) but the supplier must be aware of what materials will be needed later and when. Good forward planning can make the difference between having a well-run project with a profit and a badly run project with a loss.

Now contingency plans need to be set up, to help if the work runs behind due to poor weather, etc. As our example is not a large job, a contingency plan is not absolutely vital, but it is always advisable to have some sort of plan in place. Our job has a planned duration of only 20 days, so it is not feasible to pull contractors in from other sites. The main contingency here is to offer cash bonus incentives and overtime payments so that the work can be pulled back on track if it falls behind.

Site set-up

Although this is not a large site, and not all the amenities will be needed, there should still be a site layout plan showing where materials will be stored, and so on. A full plan for a site layout is on page 48.

Starting the work

If the planning stage has been done successfully, the materials should arrive on site a few days before the job starts so that workers and plant are not sitting around waiting.

The work being done should mirror the programme of work. The following shows how the programme is run over the 20-day contract period:

Day 1

The first thing to do on Day 1 is to set the site up and start digging the foundations. On all sites there are inductions and sometimes site meetings to discuss the contract. Calls should be made to all suppliers and sub-contractors to ensure that they are available to deliver/work on the required days, which will avoid delays to the programme through no-shows of materials or labour.

Day 2

Digging of the foundations should continue and be completed. The delivery of the materials and plant required for the foundations should arrive.

Day 3

The labour required to lay the foundations should arrive first thing in the morning and the laying of the foundations should be started. The materials and plant required for the cabling, piping, etc. should arrive.

Day 4

The site starts to get busier and the foundations should be finished today. The cabling and piping of the services should start.

Day 5

The cabling should be finished and ready to connect to the new structure. The materials for building the outer walls should arrive today, ready for Day 6.

Day 6

The bricklayers arrive on site and start to build the walls up to DPC height.

Day 7

The bricklayers finish building up to DPC height.

Day 8

The outer walls start to be built to finished height and the materials for laying the concrete floor should arrive.

Day 9

The outer walls continue to be built up and the concrete ground floor can be started.

Day 10

The outer walls continue to be built up and the concrete ground floor will be finished.

The programme should ideally be monitored every day. Now you are at the halfway stage, it is a good time to take stock: if the project is running behind, put your contingency plans into action now and if the project is ahead of schedule, see if materials, labour, etc. can be brought forward.

Days 10 and 11

The construction of the outer walls continues.

Day 12

The construction of the outer walls is completed and the materials for the roofing should arrive on site.

Day 13

The carpenters arrive on site and fit the roof trusses.

Day 14

The roofing contractors arrive on site and start to clad the roof with felt, tiles, etc. The materials for laying the floor should arrive.

Day 15

The site gets busy again as the roofers finish cladding the roof and the carpenters are back on site to lay the upper floor joists. The external doors and windows should arrive on site along with the materials for plumbing and electrical first fix.

Day 16

The flooring will be laid and the exterior windows and doors will start to be fitted. The plumber and electrician will arrive on site and start first fitting the pipes, cables, etc. The staircase will arrive on site along with the garage door and materials for painting the exterior woodwork.

Day 17

The exterior windows and doors will be finished and the main garage door will be fitted. The staircase along with all handrails, etc. will also be fitted today and the plumber and electrician will have finished their first fix. The painters will start painting the exterior of the garage and materials for the stud partitions and second fix plumbing/electrical work will arrive on site.

Day 18

The stud partitions will be built and the walls and ceilings will all be clad with plasterboard. The painter will finish the exterior work and the plumber and electrician can start their second fix work. Materials for all the internal paint and woodwork will arrive on site.

Day 19

The cladding of all the walls, ceilings etc. will be finished, as will the second fix plumbing and electrical work. The internal doors and second fix carpentry will also be done today. The internal painting work will be started.

Day 20

The internal painting work will be finished and the site will be tidied up ready for the handover to the client.

Completing the job

Now that the contract has been completed and the site cleaned up, it is time to invoice the client for the work carried out (on some larger jobs you may decide to use stage payments). For a company just starting out, this is a good time to take pictures of the work (asking the client's permission first), to show future clients the standard achieved. This is also the time to file all the drawings, invoices, costs, etc. for future reference.

On the job: Project managing

Bill and Nelson are running the job of building the garage. They look at the programme of work and notice that the painters aren't required until day 17. Bill thinks it might be a good idea to get the painters on site a couple of days early so that they can be painting as soon as possible. Nelson disagrees and thinks that could cause problems. Who do you agree with? What could be the outcome of having the painters in early?

FAQ

What can be done if a client changes their mind and wants something different?

A variation order and confirmation notice should be used to track the changes. The contractor must be sure to record all extra or different work, which will not have been included in the original pricing.

How many different plans/drawings do I need?

As many as are required to show the contractor what is to be built and how.

What does 500 people days mean?

500 people days refer to the number of people on site for a certain number of days. For example if you have 500 people on site for one day, that is 500 people days; if you have 1 person on site for 500 days then that is also 500 people days.

FAQ

What if it rains for the entire 20-day duration of the job?

The job would be seriously behind schedule. You can't plan for the weather in this country, but it would be unwise to start this job during a rainy season. There are companies that can provide scaffolding with a fitted canopy to protect the work area, which would be ideal for a job of this size. Larger jobs have longer programmes, and when they are drawn up they are made more flexible to allow for a lot of rainy days.

Knowledge check

1. What is the local authority responsible for?
2. Give a brief description of either of the two methods that can be used by a client when planning a contract.
3. What else can be offered with a tender to help win a contract?
4. State three pieces of information that can be obtained from a programme of work.
5. Why is it a good idea to take photos of the finished job?

chapter 5

Thin joint masonry construction

OVERVIEW

Thin joint construction methods were first introduced into the UK back in the mid 1980s. Although a preferred method of construction throughout much of Europe, it still remains under-utilised by the UK construction industry; the majority of house building projects still favour the traditional brick and aggregate concrete block methods. This chapter is intended to provide you with an insight into both the concept and installation methods of the thin joint block system and will cover the following:

- Features of the thin joint system
- Forms of construction where the thin joint system can be used
- Materials and components used within the thin joint system
- Tools and equipment used within thin joint systems
- Methods of construction using the thin joint system.

Definition

Aircrete – a product name for blocks manufactured from autoclaved aerated concrete

Features of the thin joint system

Tests carried out by leading manufacturers and suppliers of thin joint systems and representatives of the industry have concluded that the benefits of the thin joint system are invaluable to an industry where clients, developers and external agencies continue to demand increased production but at the same time demand improved quality of the end product.

Benefits of the thin joint system

The thin joint method uses a combination of lightweight Aircrete blocks and a fine sand and cement based, quick drying mortar. These materials are dealt with in more detail later in this chapter on page 72–74.

The main benefits of using the thin joint system include:

- speed
- improved quality of the finished product.

Speed

Definition

Swimming effect – this is where the blocks which have been laid, float on the wet mortar bed as the weight upon them increases. This dramatically affects the setting time of the block work structure and restricts the height to which blocks can be laid in any one day

Block work structure can be constructed much more quickly than traditional methods. This is due to a number of factors:

- The quick bonding time of the mortar which reduces the 'swimming effect' caused by the weight of the block work on the courses below.
- The accuracy and the uniformity of the Aircrete blocks, combined with the accuracy of the thin joint, reduces the time spent on levelling individual blocks.
- With less mortar being used, the bond strength of the block work is enhanced. This again allows for more stability during the construction process and allows other aspects of the construction work to continue within a short space of time, after the block work structure has been completed.
- The thin joint system enables the inner leaf of a cavity wall structure to be built, in its entirety, prior to the outer leaf being built. This makes it possible to provide a waterproof work environment for other trades to carry on with the work programme.
- The availability of larger format blocks also increases the speed at which walls can be built.

Improved quality of the finished product

The quality of the finished product is improved due to a number of factors:

- Aircrete blocks are produced to very accurate sizes resulting in the finished product having a cleaner and more uniform appearance.
- As the inner leaf of cavity structures can be built first it is easier to maintain a clean cavity and avoid the bridging of wall ties with mortar.

- The thermal insulation properties of the structure are improved as there is a greater area of block work due to the thinner mortar joints being used. Where the larger format blocks are used this further reduces the use of mortar.
- Aircrete blocks have high sound insulation properties due to the material used and the structure of the block.
- There is less wastage of materials due to the ease and accuracy with which the blocks can be cut. Also the thin joint mortar is supplied pre-mixed in 25 kg bags allowing for just the right amount of mortar to be mixed for the job in hand, as and when required.

Remember

As there is less mortar used with the thin joint system, more blocks will need to be ordered per metre squared, when estimating for a project using a standard sized block

Forms of construction where the thin joint system can be used

The structure and composition of Aircrete blocks makes them a very versatile material. When they are used in conjunction with the thin joint mortars which are now available, the thin joint system becomes suitable for most aspects of construction normally associated with the more traditional types of materials. The thin joint system can be used for any of the following:

- foundations
- partition walling
- external solid walling
- cavity walling
- separating or party walls.

As the thin joint system has high resistance to both water penetration and frost, few problems are encountered when it is used for external solid walling. However, it is recommended that the external face of the block work is finished with either cladding or a traditional rendered finish, particularly where the wall is constantly exposed to inclement weather e.g. rain and frost.

Note

Standard block size is 440 mm x 215 mm

FAQ

Can Aircrete blocks be used for external walls but not be finished with render or cladding?

Yes, in certain instances, such as where the external wall is built very close to an existing wall and it is difficult to provide a finish. This new wall will not be too exposed to the elements and will be protected to a high degree by the shelter provided by the existing wall.

The thin joint system also has a high resistance to fire and good sound insulation qualities making it highly suitable for the construction of partition walling and separating walls.

The strength and sulphate resistant properties of the system also make it suitable for foundation walls in most types of soil and ground conditions.

Materials and components used within the thin joint system

Aircrete blocks

These are made from autoclaved aerated concrete. This is a lightweight material which makes the blocks both easy to handle and to cut but at the same time has a high compressive strength. The main ingredients which are combined to form this material are lime, sand of quartz, water and cement. As part of the name suggests, Aircrete is made up of between 60% and 80% air by volume, with thousands of tiny air bubbles being produced during the 'baking' process. Once this process is complete and the material has been allowed to set it is cut into the required size blocks by the use of mechanical wires. In order to obtain the maximum strength of the blocks they are cured in autoclaves. This is where the blocks are subjected to saturation with high pressured steam at up to 200°C.

Aircrete blocks are available in a variety of sizes ranging from the standard sized block up to an extra large block with a face size of approx 610 mm x 270 mm. These blocks are also available in varying thicknesses and grades, to suit the work being carried out.

Aircrete blocks

Safety tip

Always remember the basics of kinetic lifting techniques when handling blocks, particularly the larger size blocks available with the thin joint system

Note

Data on fire resistance, 'U' values and handling weights of various types of Aircrete blocks can be obtained from the various manufacturers using their technical helplines

Definition

'U' values – these indicate the thermal performance of a material in different situations

Thin joint mortar

Thin joint mortar is a combination of fine ground sand (silica) and Portland cements. Thin joint mortar is available under a number of different trade names and is produced by various manufacturers as part of their thin joint systems. Thin joint mortar is normally supplied in 25 kg bags and is added to water and mixed until the correct consistency is obtained. Guidance for mixing is given on the packaging. Thin joint mortars remain workable for a number of hours, up to 4 hours in most instances, whilst still in the bucket. However, once spread on the block the mortar will begin to set within 10 to 20 minutes. Full setting of the mortar is reached after approximately 1 to 2 hours, depending on the product itself. Thin joint mortar is spread at a thickness of 2-3 mm. Tools used for the mixing and application of the mortar are explained later in this chapter.

Safety tip

It is recommended that you use suitable hand protection when using thin joint mortar. As this type of mortar is cement-based, there is a risk of developing dermatitis and/or burns and irritation to the skin, through prolonged exposure to the mortar

Wall ties for thin joint systems

Wall ties used in traditional brick and block structures are not suitable for use in the thin joint systems as they are too thick to fit into the thin mortar joints. However, there are a variety of thin joint compatible ties currently on the market. The majority of ties are made from stainless steel. Some of the most common include:

- twist ties
- flat steel ties
- abutment wall ties
- movement joint ties.

Did you know?

Although occasional stirring or remixing of the thin joint mortar can be carried out following the initial mix, no additional water should be added to thin joint mortar as this will significantly weaken the bonding properties of the mix

Twist ties

These are used for cavity walls where the inner leaf has been built and the outer leaf is still under construction. These ties are driven into the Aircrete block work at a height to suit the outer leaf courses as they are laid. These ties will also take insulation clips, which secure partial fill cavity insulation bats. Twist ties are available in various sizes to suit up to 150 mm cavities.

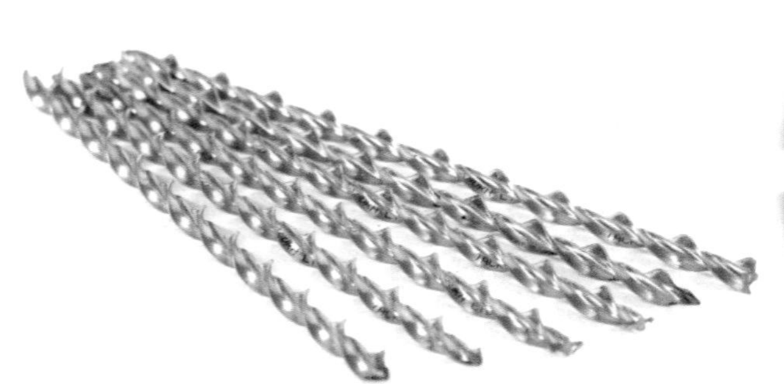

Twist tie

Insulation clips/discs

Flat steel ties

These are available for use when joining the inner and outer leaf of a cavity wall where the two leaves are constructed at the same time and are of the same course height. These ties are bedded into the block work in the same way as traditional methods.

Flat steel type wall ties

These flat steel ties are also available for connecting block work at junctions, i.e. where perimeter walls join partition or dividing walls.

Abutment wall ties

Abutment wall tie

These are also used for connecting block work at junctions where courses are not at the same level. The tie is fixed to the perimeter wall using a suitable fixing and the other end of the tie sits into the bed joint of the adjoining wall.

Find out

If there are any variations to the ties mentioned, which are suited to the thin joint system?

Movement joint ties

As the name suggests these are used to tie walls together where the continuous length has been broken up to allow for movement joints. These ties allow for contraction and expansion between the two walls to avoid damage to the block work caused by movement.

Movement tie

Tools and equipment used with the thin joint system

Scoop

This is used to spread thin joint mortar producing a consistent joint thickness of 2-3 mm. The scoop is available in varying sizes of between 75-200 mm.

Scoops

Sledge

As with the scoop this tool is also used to spread thin join mortar. However, this is for use where the width of the block exceeds 200 mm. The sledge is available in sizes between 200-300 mm.

Sledge

Masonry hand saw

This is used to cut Aircrete blocks to the required size.

Block cutting square

This is used as a marking guide when cutting blocks.

Note

On large sites or in instances where a large number of cuts are required for the job a mechanical hand saw or circular saw may be used to cut blocks

Masonry hand saw

Block cutting square

Sanding board

The sanding board is used to remove any imperfections in the bed course. As the thin joint system requires a very accurate bed thickness to be maintained, it is important that any raised areas in the bed course are removed prior to applying the thin mortar joint.

Sanding board

Block rasp

The block rasp is used to trim any areas of the block which are raised and are too big to be removed with a sanding board. These raised areas may occur when there has been inaccurate cutting and will affect the accuracy of the thin joint thickness.

Block rasp

Whisk attachment

The whisk is attached to a powered drill and is used to mix the thin joint mortar in a large tub or bucket.

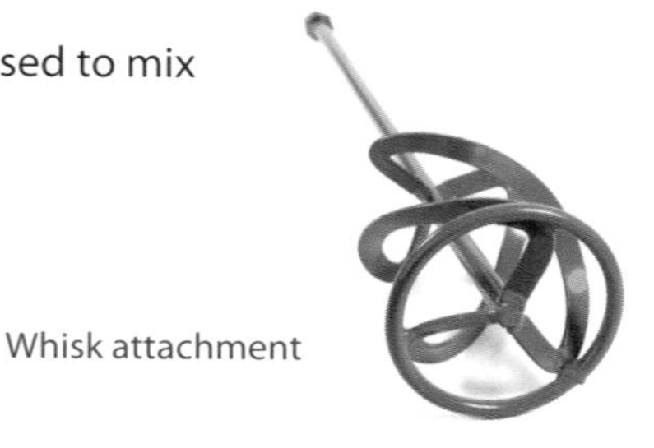

Whisk attachment

Methods of construction using the thin joint system

If constructing a cavity wall structure, it is important to ensure that the substructure walls are built up to the damp proof course (DPC) prior to laying the inner thin joint block work. This enables any required openings to be set out accurately before work starts on the superstructure.

In most cases the first course or 'bed course' in the thin joint system should be laid using the normal sand/cement mortar. This will take out any inaccuracies that are present within the floor slab or foundation masonry.

In order to maintain accuracy in the courses above the bed course, thin joint mortar may be used for the perpends (vertical joints) of the bed course. Once the bed course is sufficiently stable, work with the thin joint system can commence.

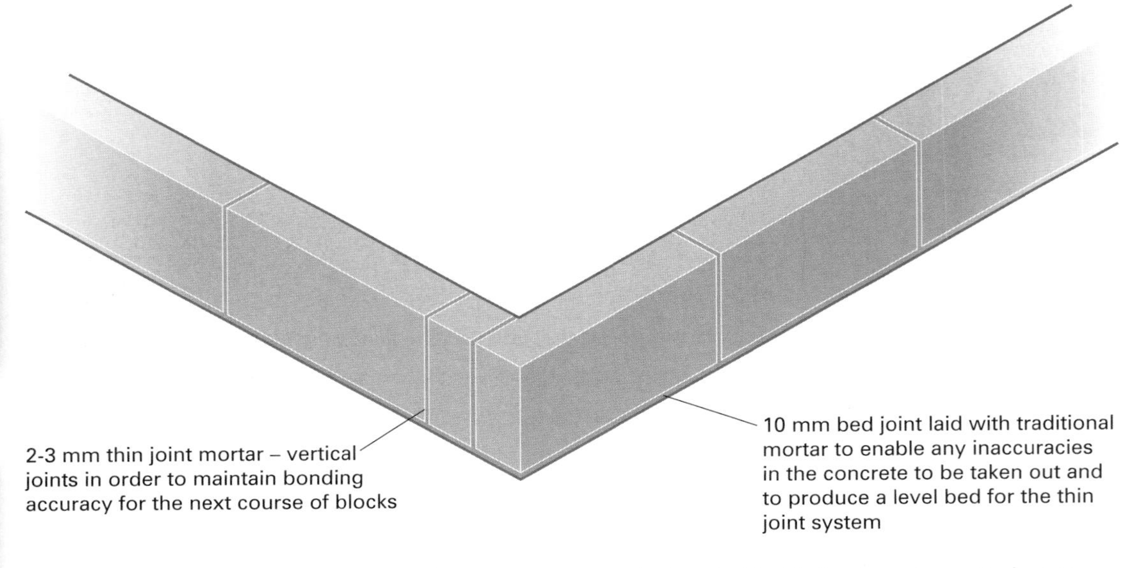

Figure 5.1 A bed course of blocks laid with traditional mortar bed and with thin joint mortar vertical joints

As mentioned, bonding arrangements and the installation methods are much the same as the traditional block laying methods. These are described in *Brickwork Level 2*.

When erecting the corners of block walls built using the thin joint system, it is vitally important to ensure accuracy in the levelling, plumbing and gauging of the blocks. With the thin joint system there is no option of being able to open up joints to compensate for inaccuracies you might have caused during the build.

Once the corners have been erected the blocks can be run into a line as normal. The thin joint mortar is applied to the blocks using a scoop or a sledge dependant on the width of the block (see the description of these tools on p74). Both the scoop and the sledge provide a consistent 2-3 mm layer of mortar across both the bed and vertical joints.

Note

Bond arrangements for the thin joint system are the same as those used in the traditional brick and block methods

Definition

Superstructure - work above DPC

Remember

It is essential that the bed course is level and free from imperfections prior to laying the first bed of the thin joint mortar

Note

You must always ensure that the course which is to receive a bed of thin joint mortar is free from dust, as this can adversely affect the adhesion of the mortar

FAQ

Can thin joint mortar be used in conjunction with ordinary brickwork construction?

No, as this is specifically designed for use with Aircrete material.

Using a scoop

Using a sledge

As the individual blocks are laid, each block should be firmly pushed against the vertical, mortared face of the previously laid block and at the same time lowered onto the mortared bed below. It is important to ensure that full joints are maintained at all times, to retain the effectiveness and stability of the thin joint system. Where there is a need to tap blocks into place to ensure full uniform joints that are accurately laid to the line, a rubber mallet should be used in order to prevent damage to the blocks.

As previously stated, when constructing cavity walls the inner leaf can be built in its entirety, prior to work commencing on the outer leaf. This has a number of advantages:

- a watertight structure is provided at a much earlier stage of the project
- partial or full fill insulation can be fitted much more easily and not affected by excess mortar protruding from joints
- wall ties can be fixed once the insulation is in place - the insulation is then secured by the wall tie being driven through into the pre-erected block work and secured with suitable insulation clips
- it is easier to keep a clean cavity as the outer leaf is constructed.

Did you know?

Where a single skin of walling is built in its entirety and it is not supported by other walls, it should be supported or propped up until the mortar has fully set and is sufficiently stable. If this is not done, particularly during adverse weather conditions, the wall may collapse

Note

Where wall ties are to be driven into the newly constructed inner leaf it is recommended that the block work has been stabilised by the installation of the floor joists at the head of the wall

Note

The spacing of wall ties is the same as that for the traditional methods used when constructing cavity walling

Lintels

When forming openings for windows and doors, manufacturers of the thin joint system recommend the use of either box type or combination type lintels. However, where a combination type lintel is used this will need to be supported with props until the outer leaf is constructed. This will prevent the lintel tipping forward. It is also recommended that lintels be bedded using traditional mortar and joint thickness to allow for any discrepancies within the lintels' design.

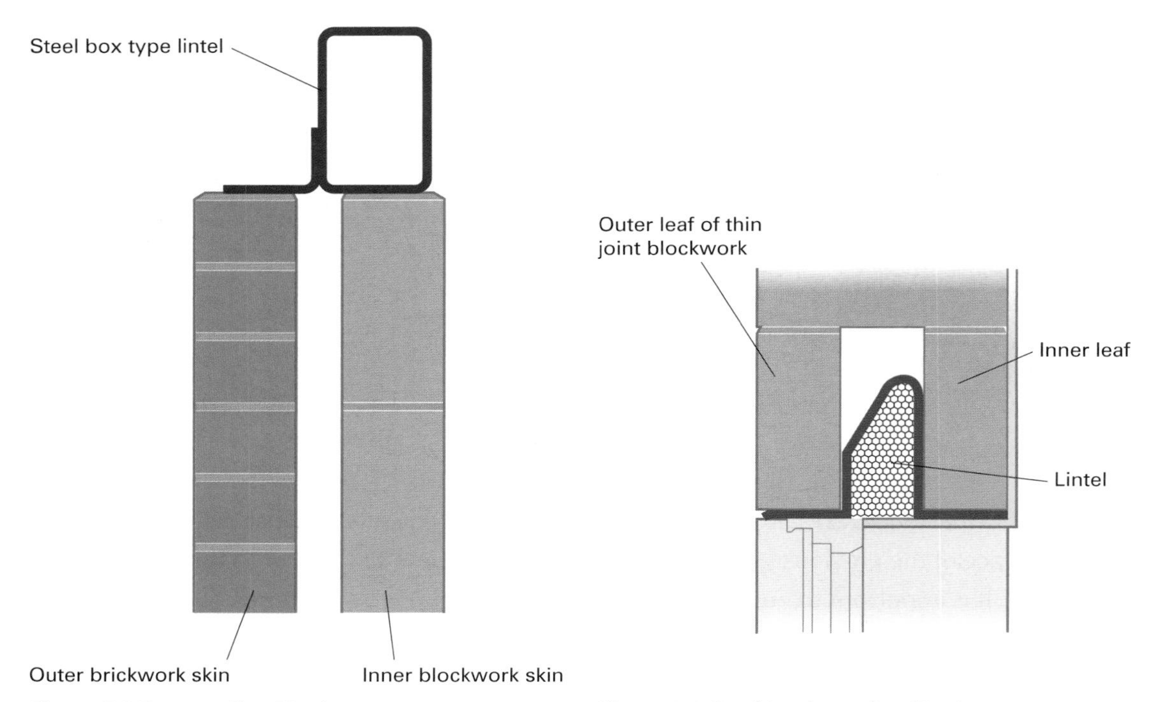

Figure 5.2 Box type lintel in situ

Figure 5.3 Combined type lintel in situ

Reveals

Reveals are formed in much the same way as with traditional construction methods. The Aircrete blocks can be cut to the required dimensions of the reveal, however the first reveal block may require support to enable the remaining blocks to be laid on top.

Find out

Are there any other materials from which reinforcement for thin joint systems can be made?

Tensile stress

Where the block work is likely to be subjected to tensile forces (being stretched) reinforcement can be built into the horizontal bed of the thin joint walling. However, only reinforcement material specially designed for use with the thin joint system should be used. This is widely available and is supplied in rolls of up to 50 m in length. Thin joint reinforcement is made from either stainless steel wire or galvanised steel with a zinc coating. The thickness of this reinforcement is approximately1.2 mm and is bedded within the thin joint mortar.

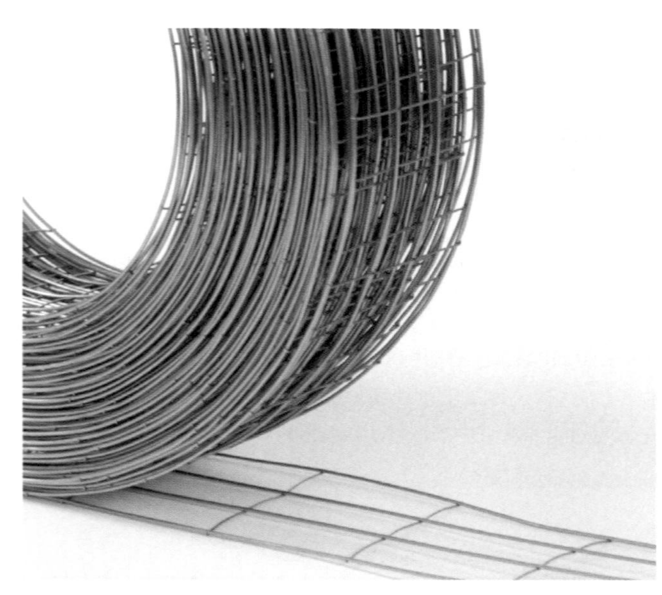
Reinforcement materials available for use in thin joint systems

During use, where there is a need to overlap the reinforcement, this overlap should be a minimum of 225 mm. Where the reinforcement is used around openings it should extend to at least 600 mm into the block work on either side of the opening.

Reinforcement can be used in lengths of thin joint block work over 6 m as an alternative to using movement joints. This is particularly effective for separating walls where movement joints cannot be used.

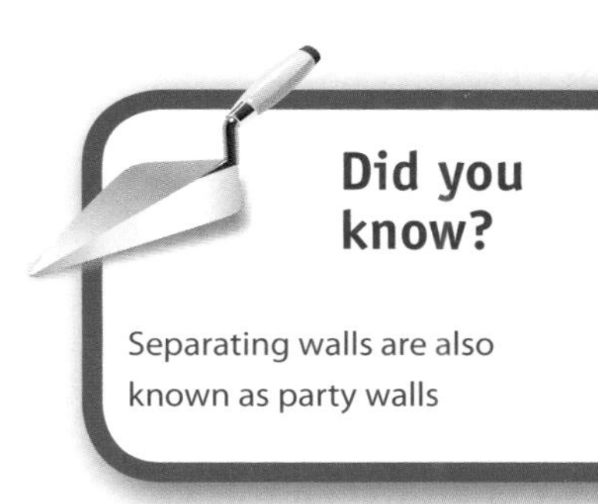

Did you know?

Separating walls are also known as party walls

Find Out

What is the maximum vertical distance between ties when used in a movement joint?

Movement joints

Where the design of the structure requires the use of movement joints, manufacturers of Aircrete blocks recommend the following:

- the first movement joint should be no more than 3 m from a corner of the fixed end
- long lengths of walling should be made up of separate panels of lengths of not more than 6 m.

Movement joints can be formed by either introducing 10 mm gaps between the panels and filling with fibre boards or by the use of specially designed ties which connect two panels together but allow movement of any panel that is subjected to tensile stress.

These specially designed ties are also available for use when tying walls together at junctions e.g. where partition walls meet with perimeter walls, particularly those junctions which are susceptible to movement.

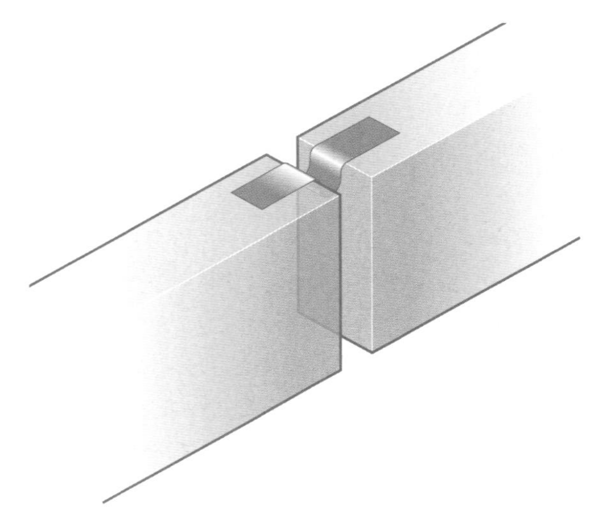
Figure 5.4 The use of movement ties

On the job: Freddy's dilemma

A gang of bricklayers responsible for constructing the thin joint block work on site have not turned up for work. There is one internal wall left to construct, which must be finished that day as the floor joists are to be installed the following day. As the only bricklayer left on site, Freddy has been asked to complete the work. The original gang have set out and laid the first course of blocks. However, Freddy notices that this has been done using thin joint mortar and that the first course is out of level across the length. Can Freddy rectify this as the work proceeds? What should he do?

Knowledge check

1. What are the two main benefits of the thin joint system?
2. What is meant by the term 'swimming effect'?
3. Why are the thermal properties of the structure improved using the thin joint system?
4. What is the composite material from which Aircrete blocks are made?
5. What is the size of the mortar bed used in the thin joint system?
6. What tool is used to spread thin joint mortar on blocks up to 200 mm in width?
7. What is used to remove any large imperfections in cut blocks?
8. What tool should be used where there is a need to tap blocks to aid levelling and maintain full joints?
9. What is the maximum distance from a corner of a wall at which a movement joint should be incorporated?
10. What is the minimum overlap that is required when using horizontal masonry reinforcement?

chapter 6

Complex masonry structures

OVERVIEW

'Complex masonry structures' refers to any brickwork or stone work which requires intricate, and sometimes difficult, setting out procedures. It also refers to brickwork or stone work where decorative features have been included within a structure to provide support or enhance aesthetic value (aesthetic means 'the principles of beauty, taste and art'). We will deal with one of the main methods of providing decorative features in Chapter 9. In this chapter we will look at other methods of including decorative features, along with the more intricate setting out details required for work such as curved brickwork and angled brickwork.
Included in this chapter are:

- Recessed and projecting brickwork including corbelling, string courses, soldier courses, dog toothing and dentil courses
- Diaper work
- Curved work
- Angled and splayed brickwork (including raking cuts)
- Special shaped bricks.

Corbelling and soldier courses

Recessed and projecting brickwork

Remember

Good planning and setting out is essential as there is very little room for error in complex and decorative brickwork. Materials should also be carefully selected, as flawed or sub-standard materials will be even more visible when the feature in which they are used is the main focal point for the untrained eye

Did you know

Corbelling is commonly used to form the shoulders of gable ends

Corbelling

Traditionally corbelling is a method of providing structural support for brickwork which is to extend out in front of the main walling. However, corbelling details have also been used to enhance the appearance of brickwork structures for many years.

All types of corbelling work must be carefully planned and carried out to satisfy both the structural design requirements of the project and the British Standards Institution Codes of Practice.

Corbelling can be used at certain positions in a length of walling or can be continuous throughout the length of the walling.

Note

Failure to plan effectively and follow the requirements for bonding of corbelling bricks can result in weak support for the structure and quite possibly collapse of the corbelling feature and any work it supports

Corbelling used as the shoulder of a gable end

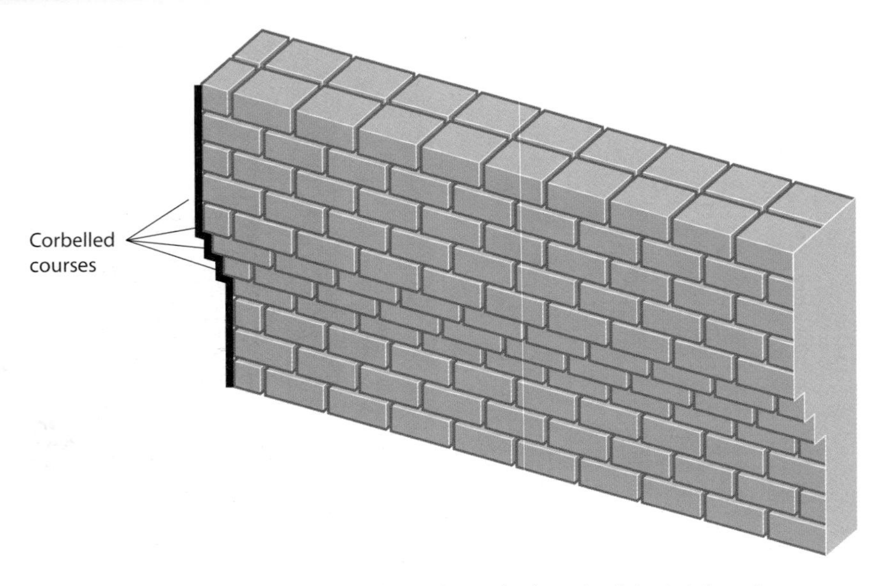

Figure 6.1 Corbelling used throughout the length of the brickwork structure

Corbelling at a certain position in a length of walling

Methods for constructing corbels

The overhang measurement for each course of a brick corbel should be equal. In all instances, the measurement shown on the detailed drawing provided by the architect should be adhered to. However the two most common measurements used for the overhang of individual courses is either 28 mm or 56 mm.

It is essential when constructing a corbel that plumb and level are accurately maintained. It is also important to maintain equal projections for each course and as a rule of thumb, the total projection of the entire corbel should not exceed the thickness of the main wall.

When tying the corbel bricks into the main wall, you should endeavour to achieve the maximum lap with the course below and wherever possible headers should be used for the corbelled bricks, particularly for a corbel where larger projections are used (quarter brick overhang).

When building any corbel it is important to lay the bricks from the back of the main wall through to the front of the corbel. This allows the back of the corbelled bricks below to be held or weighted down as quickly as possible to prevent them tipping forward.

The photographs below show the preferred bonding arrangements for a corbel with a quarter brick overhang per course.

Note

The greater the overhang the more difficulty there is in preventing tipping of the bricks during construction

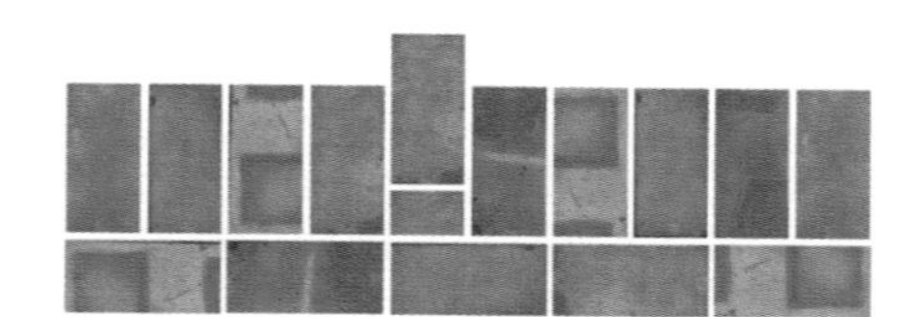

Course 1

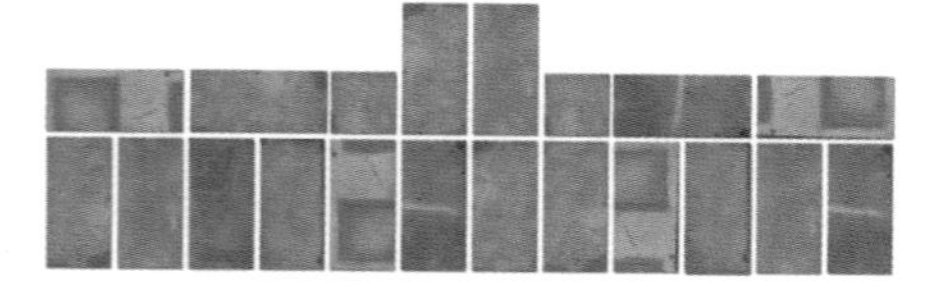

Course 2

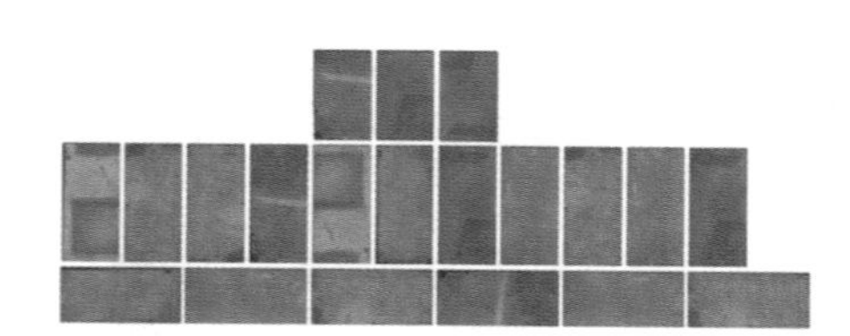

Course 3

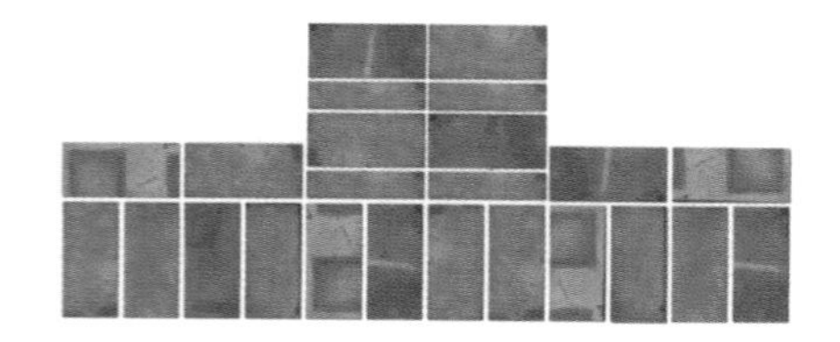

Course 4

Completed corbelling

As each course is constructed the bricklayer must ensure that the corbel is square to the main wall. This can be achieved with the aid of a building square.

It is also important that each course is levelled on the underside of the corbelled bricks as this is the line that will be seen.

Where a continuous corbel is being built a line is used on the underside edge of the corbel to maintain a straight edge.

Using a building square

Good idea

Always tilt the front corbel bricks backwards slightly as they are laid – this can help prevent tipping. The brick can be truly levelled in as the next course is laid

Definition

Tipping – this is where, if care is not taken during the laying process, the whole corbel may tip forward and quite possibly topple over

String courses

String courses are normally introduced towards the top of walls, particularly at eaves level or the last few courses of large boundary walls, as a decorative feature. String courses can be built in using a variety of bonding arrangements. These include:

- soldier courses
- dog toothing
- dentil courses.

Remember

Always ensure that all bed joints and cross joints are completely full within the corbel to ensure both strength and stability

A dentil course

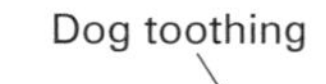

Dog toothing

Did you know

Dog toothing can also be used to form decorative panels

String courses are sometimes used lower down in the face of the wall as a decorative feature. However these are more commonly known as 'band courses'. The most common arrangement used for band courses is a soldier course.

String courses can also be formed using specially shaped bricks, of which there are numerous types and variations.

Wherever string courses are constructed above normal 'eye-line' the bricks used in these courses must be lined up along their bottom edge as opposed to the top edge. This ensures that the underneath of the feature, the edge that will be seen, appears straight and seamless.

Soldier courses

Soldier courses are simply bricks laid on end next to each other. However, unless great care is taken to ensure soldier bricks are laid both plumb and level across the length of the course, the finished article can be unsightly.

When laying soldier courses, a line must be used along the top edge of the soldier course throughout the construction. In addition, a small spirit level or boat level must be used to ensure that the individual soldiers are kept plumb. Just one brick out of plumb will affect the line and result in a poor finish to the feature.

Soldier courses used as decorative features

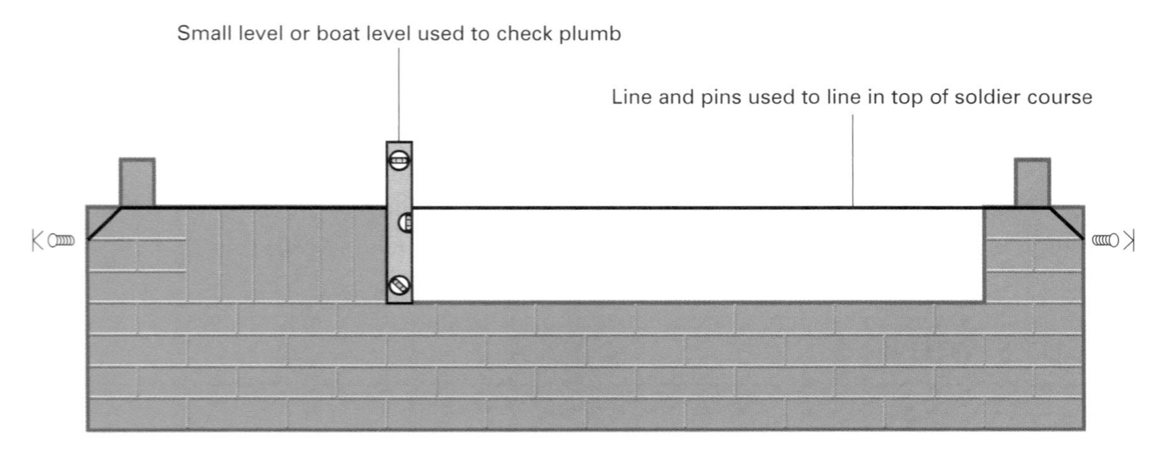

Figure 6.2 Using a brick line and boat level to construct a soldier course

Dog toothing

Dog toothing refers to a bonding arrangement in which the bricks are laid at a 45° angle to the main face of the wall. This type of bonding arrangement can either project from the main face or can be built flush with the main face. By building the edge of the angled bricks flush with the main wall, a recessed effect will be produced.

When constructing a course of projecting dog toothing the projecting bricks must be lined in by fixing a brick line across the face of the bricks. The brick line will maintain even projection along the length of the feature. The use of a spirit level placed against the underside of the projecting course will ensure the 'seen edge' (the underside edge of the feature) remains straight and even to the eye.

Note

Once the first brick has been cut at the correct angle (45°), this can then be used as a template for all of the other cuts

Note

It is important to ensure that straight joints are avoided whenever possible

Dentil courses

A dentil course refers to a string course where alternate headers in the same course are projected from the face of the wall. The same principles apply as for dog toothing when constructing a dentil course in that the underside of the bricks are to be levelled as the work progresses and the brick line is to be fixed across the face of the bricks being laid.

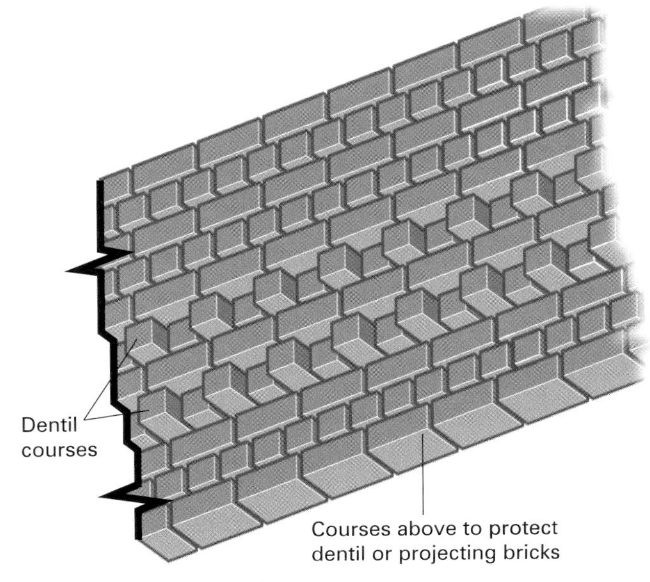

Figure 6.3 A dentil course

Both dog toothing and dentil courses should always be finished off with a course of bricks above them. These courses can either be laid flush with the feature course or project out past the feature.

This additional course is intended to finish off the feature and provide protection from the elements and possible damage to face and upper edges of the feature bricks.

Diaper work

Did you know

Diaper work refers to the forming of diamond-shaped patterns

Diaper bond is quite simply the forming of diamond patterns within the face of a length of walling. This type of work provides no more than decorative value to a building.

The diamond patterns are formed using contrasting bricks to those of the main walling and incorporated as recessed, projecting or flush to the face.

Diaper bond

There are numerous variations to the patterns which can be formed. Normally patterns are formed using headers, as the use of stretchers is more difficult in relation to maintaining bond and does not provide the same uniformed diamond effect.

Whenever projecting diaper bond is used it is important to remember that all projecting bricks must be plumbed to ensure equal projection throughout the pattern. The projections should be plumbed both on the face and side elevations.

When producing a recessed diaper bond pattern it is advisable to use a depth gauge or template to ensure that the recess depth is maintained throughout the pattern. These gauges can be made from timber notched to the exact depth required for the recess.

Curved brickwork

Brickwork can be curved either on plan or in elevation. Arches are a typical example of brickwork curved in elevation. This section will deal with other forms of curved work in elevation and also brickwork curved on plan.

> **Definition**
>
> **Elevation** – refers to a vertical face of a building

Brickwork curved in elevation

There are two methods of constructing curved brickwork in elevation and they are:

- convex
- concave.

> **Definition**
>
> **Concave** – means rounded inwards
>
> **Convex** – means curved outward

Constructing convex curved brickwork

This type of curved work is produced with the aid of a short length of timber pointed at one end and fixed to the face of the wall – this length of timber is referred to as a trammel.

The point at which the trammel is fixed to the face of the wall is known as the pivot point.

The trammel can be fixed to a timber plate, which is secured to the brickwork with the use of nails driven into the bed joints. When fixing the trammel to the timber plate you must ensure that it is not fixed tightly against the plate, preventing it from turning easily.

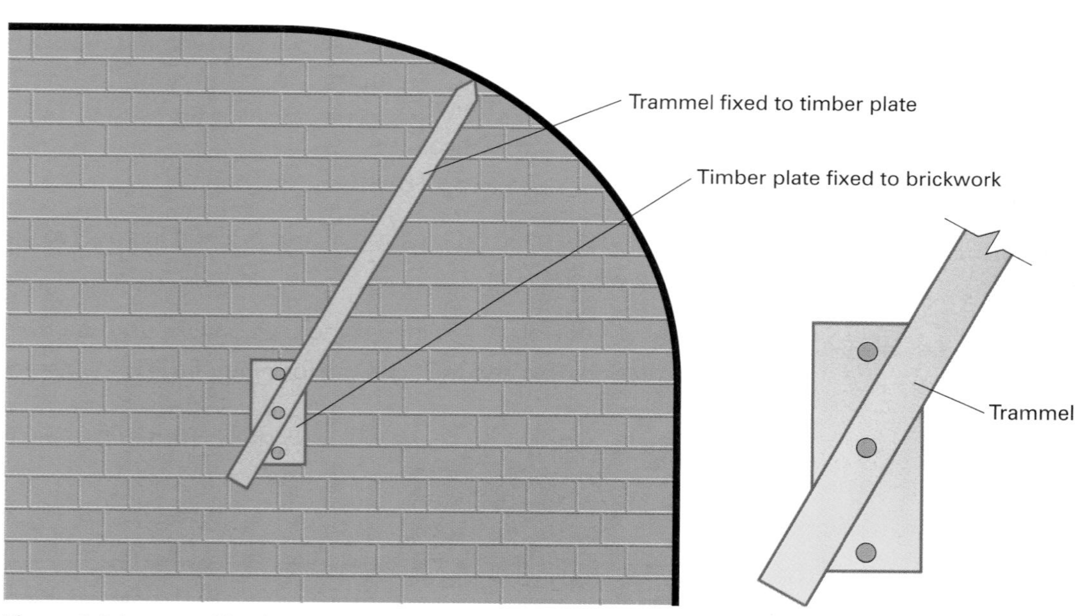

Figure 6.4 A trammel in place

The bricks to be cut in order to form the curve are placed in position, dry and on top of a piece timber or other suitable material at a thickness of 10 mm to simulate the bed joint thickness. The vertical joint thickness must also be allowed for.

The trammel is then swung round across the face of the positioned brick and marked with a pencil or suitable marker. Once the brick has been cut it can be laid and checked for accuracy by again swinging the trammel across the face.

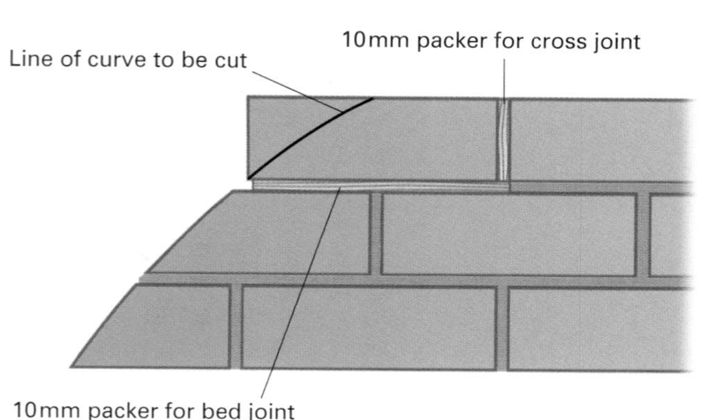

Figure 6.5 The use of a 10 mm packing to allow for joint thickness

A brick laid on edge is the most common way to provide the finish or capping to this type of curved brickwork, unless of course it is used as a decorative feature within a length of walling which is to be continued in height.

Depending on the severity of the curve, the brick-on-edge can either be laid with V-shaped joints or the bricks are cut to a V shape to prevent oversized joints.

Constructing concave curved brickwork

Again a trammel will need to be used to establish the cuts required to form the curve. However, the trammel needs to be positioned and secured in a completely different way.

Concave curved brickwork

Before the trammel can be positioned, the main walling will need to be built to the height of the striking point. Once this height has been reached the trammel can be positioned.

The trammel is fixed onto a timber support held in position on the top course by either a brick or block weight.

The same principles used in forming the convex curve are then applied to this type of construction. This also includes the forming of the brick-on-edge course.

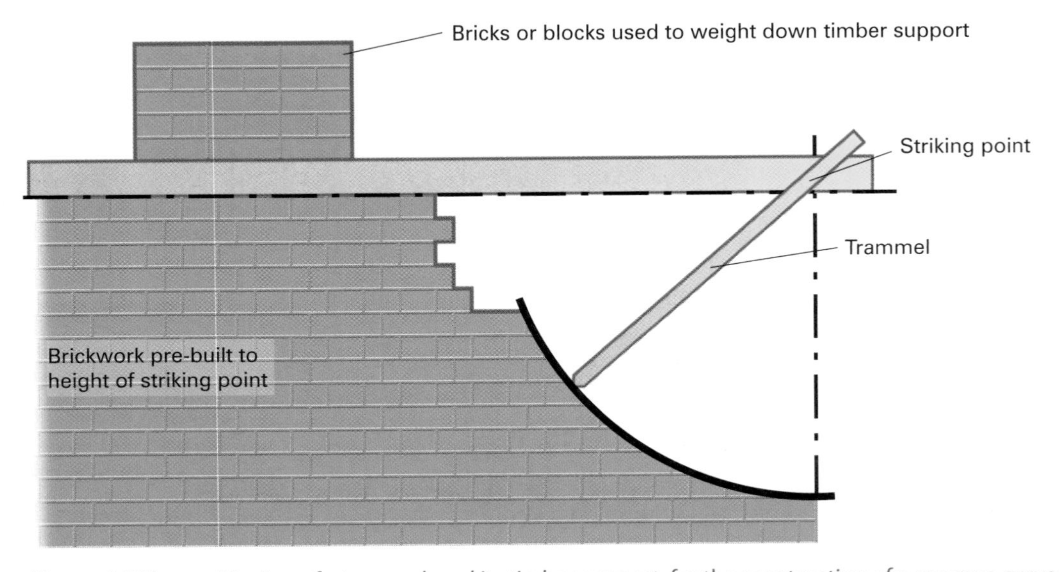

Figure 6.6 The positioning of a trammel, and its timber support, for the construction of a concave curve

Brickwork curved on plan

Brickwork which is curved on plan can be used in a number of situations. These include constructing brickwork to support bay windows, boundary walls which have to follow the curvature of roads and pathways and for numerous decorative features such as flower beds etc.

There are a number of methods used in constructing this type of walling. The choice of which method to use depends on the size of the curved wall to be built and the work space available.

However, whichever method is used, the rules for both plumbing and levelling the brickwork remain the same. With walls curved on plan it is essential that plumbing and levelling are accurate throughout the construction of the walling. If accuracy is not maintained, the end product will be unsightly and it is highly unlikely that the desired curvature of the wall will be achieved.

On any curved wall, plumbing points will need to be established at various intervals around the length of the curve. Although the length of the curve will determine the amount of plumbing points required these should be no more than 1 m to 1.2 m apart.

Levelling across the top of the wall should always be carried between the plumbing points.

Where the curves to be constructed are relatively small, a small timber template can be used. This template is cut accurately to fit around the curved face of the wall and will need to be cut to a length which allows it to fit between the plumbing points.

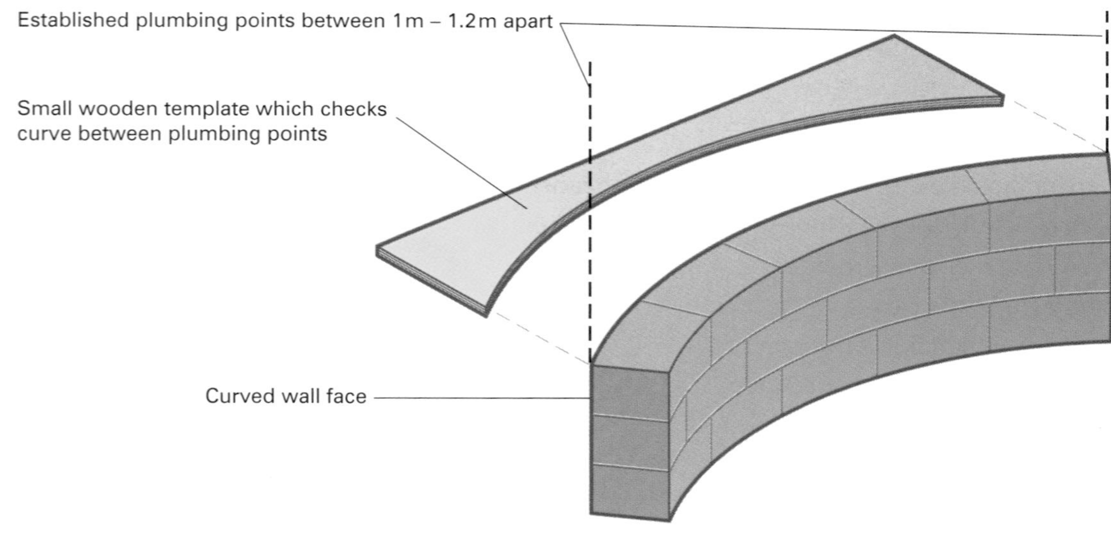

Figure 6.7 Established plumbing points and method of levelling for curved walls

Larger templates can be produced for constructing bay windows. These templates would be designed to sit on the top of each course to be built and give both the curve for the outside face of the curved bay and the line of the main wall.

Note

No matter what type of template is used, it is essential that you ensure that all bricks sit against the template when you are carrying out checks using it

The other method used to help in the construction of curved walls is the trammel. We have already seen the way in which a trammel is used to aid cutting and check the accuracy of curved walling earlier in this chapter and the principle is the same. However, a trammel can only be used where there is sufficient space to establish the pivoting point. The position of the pivot point can be determined from the detailed drawings provided on site. The trammel can be used for either the internal or external face of the curve.

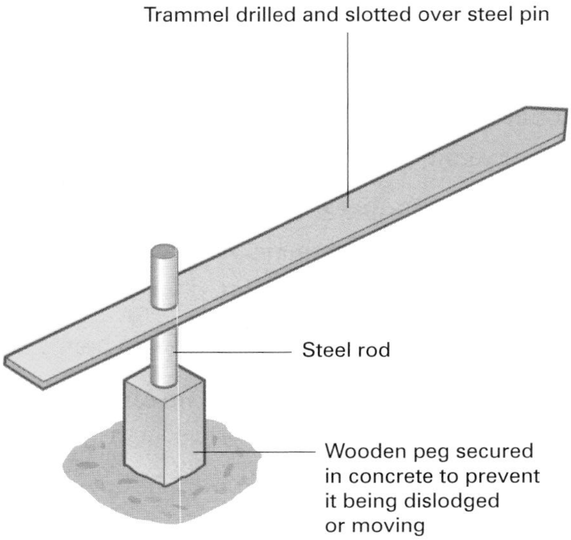

Trammel drilled and slotted over steel pin

Steel rod

Wooden peg secured in concrete to prevent it being dislodged or moving

Figure 6.8 A trammel fixed over a steel pin

The trammel is fixed by one end being drilled to allow it to be dropped over a steel pin representing the pivot point. This steel pin should be seated in the top of a wooden peg, which in turn is set in concrete to prevent it from moving whilst in use.

Although stretchers are used in curved walling, the most common bond used is header bond. Stretcher bond can be used in curved walls. However, the stretchers may have to be cut on the back face, where the curve is too tight to allow the use of full stretchers, so as not to affect the trueness of the curve.

Note

When using either stretcher or header bond, V-shaped cross-joints have to be used in order to ensure the bricks follow the desired curve line

Header bond

Depending on the severity of the curve, full headers can be used throughout the length of each course. However, where the curve is smaller or tighter, snap headers have to be used in order to maintain a true curve. Where this is the case, a full header is used every third brick. This practice prevents oversized V-shaped joints which make the wall look unsightly.

Where both sides of a curved wall need to have a good face, it is advisable to use purpose-made Radial bricks. These are available in both headers and stretchers.

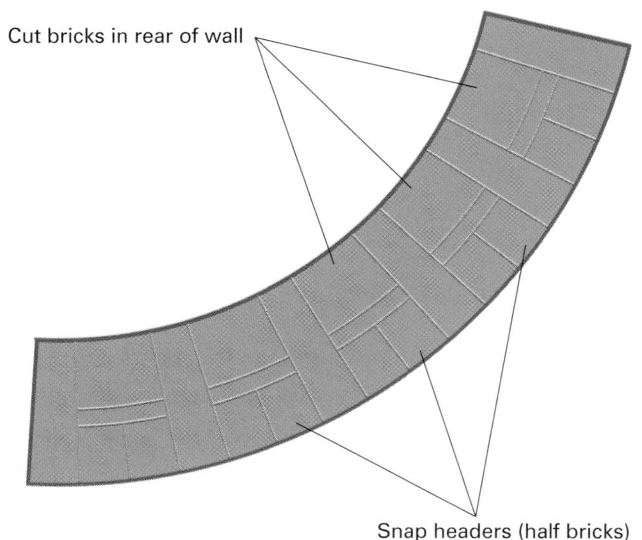

Figure 6.9 Using snap headers when constructing curved walling in header bond

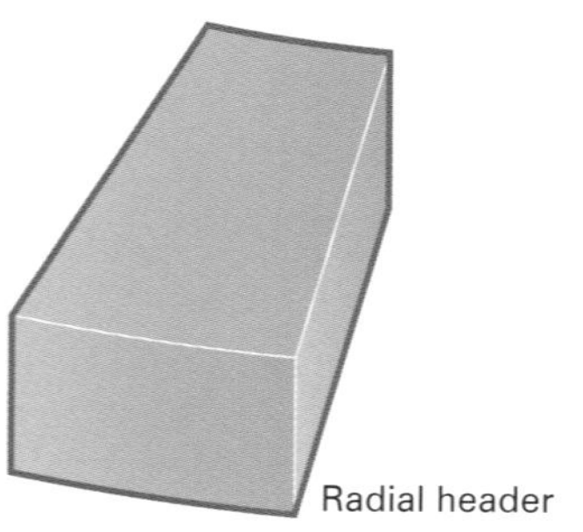

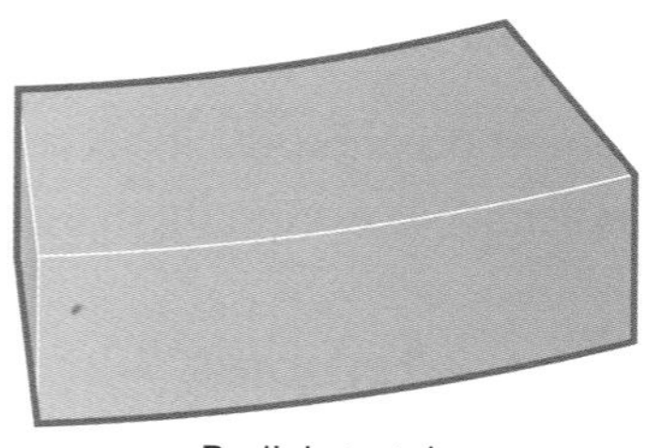

Figure 6.10 Radial header and stretcher bricks

> **Note**
>
> The use of these bricks also removes the need for V-shaped joints

Serpentine walls

As the name suggests, this type of walling turns in and out along its length giving a snaking effect. The curves are set out and constructed using the methods described earlier in this chapter.

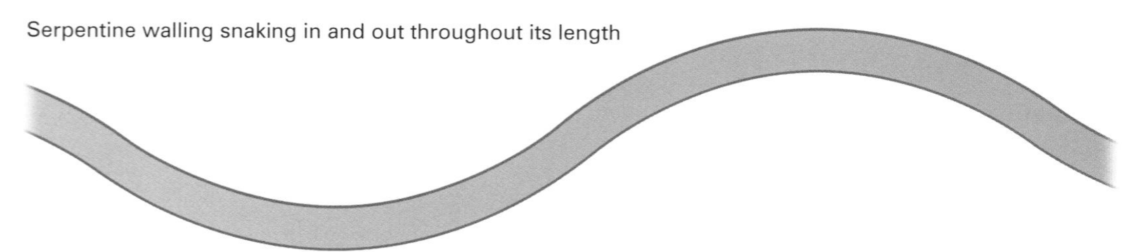

Figure 6.11 A plan view of a serpentine wall

Axed arches

Axed arches are constructed from cut bricks as opposed to the wedge or V-shaped joints used in the construction of rough ringed arches.

The use of arch construction in modern day building projects is far less common than it was and more often than not, where arch construction is incorporated into a building, purpose-made bricks are used. Purpose-made bricks remove the need for bricks to be cut on site which can be time consuming and generate a high percentage of wasted bricks through the cutting process. Another major advantage with using purpose-made voussoirs or arch-bricks is that they are uniform in shape and their dimensions are accurate.

An axed arch

However, where there is a requirement for voussoirs to be cut by hand, a template must be made to establish the shape of them. The template itself will need to be traversed across the face of the arch in order to provide the exact shape required for each of the voussoirs.

Cutting an axed arch

The traditional method of producing axed brick arches is to cut bricks to shape using a hammer and bolster, measuring them against a templet of the voussoir shape required.

How to make the templet

The tools required to make an accurate templet:

- Trammel heads
- Dividers
- Bevel
- Traversing rules
- Measuring rule
- Straight edge
- Carpenter's tools for cutting wood templet.

The templet is usually made from timber of between 6 mm and 12 mm thickness.

The first step is to draw the arch full size on a sheet of plywood.

Set out a centre line and then another line at right angles to this (known as the 'springing line'). Find out the springing point and draw intrados, extrados and skewback lines.

Set the dividers to the size of the brick being used in the arch, and mark out voussoirs on the extrados.

Based on the full size drawing of the arch, mark out the templet onto plywood, to project approximately 50 mm above the extrados and 150 mm below the intrados, which will allow for any adjustment that may be need to be made during traversing the arch.

Note

You only need to set out half of the arch, to include the key brick

Note

Once the dividers have been set, do not open them any further as any templet based on this voussoir shape will be incorrect and any bricks cut to this templet will be too narrow to fit the actual arch.

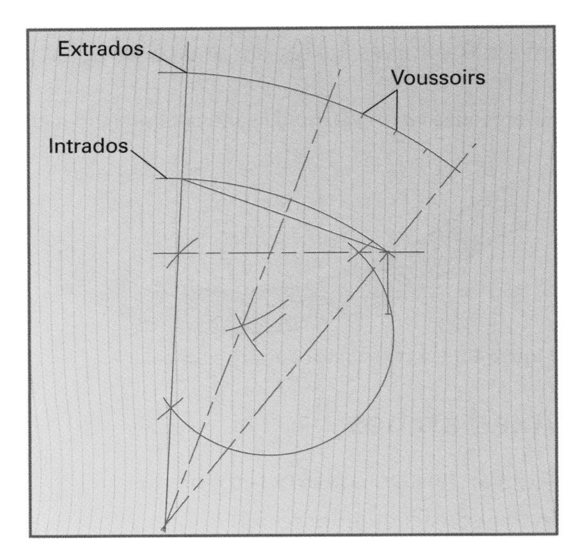

Figure 6.12 Setting out an axed arch

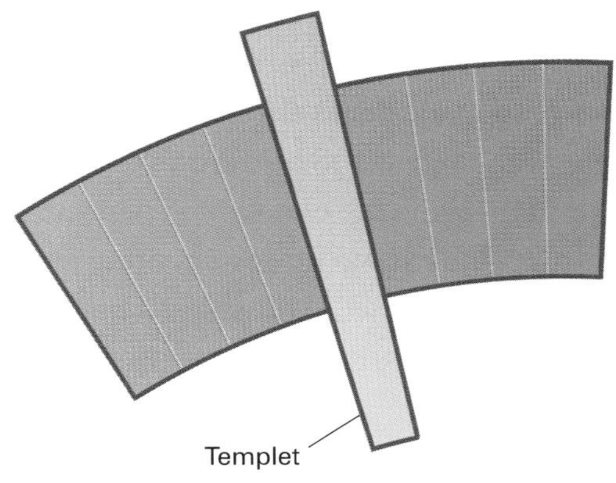

Figure 6.13 Templet

Traversing the arch

At this stage the templet only provides a rough guide. To obtain an accurate shape, the templet must be traversed over the face of the arch, to highlight any small errors in the shape.

To traverse the arch, follow the steps below.

1. Place the traversing rule A to the key brick.
2. Arrange the templet to fit a voussoir and mark a line on the side of the templet to coincide with the intrados. This is called the 'traversing mark'.
3. Place the traversing rule B.
4. Remove A and the templet.
5. Place A to B
6. Remove B and again fit templet, allowing traversing mark to coincide with the intrados.

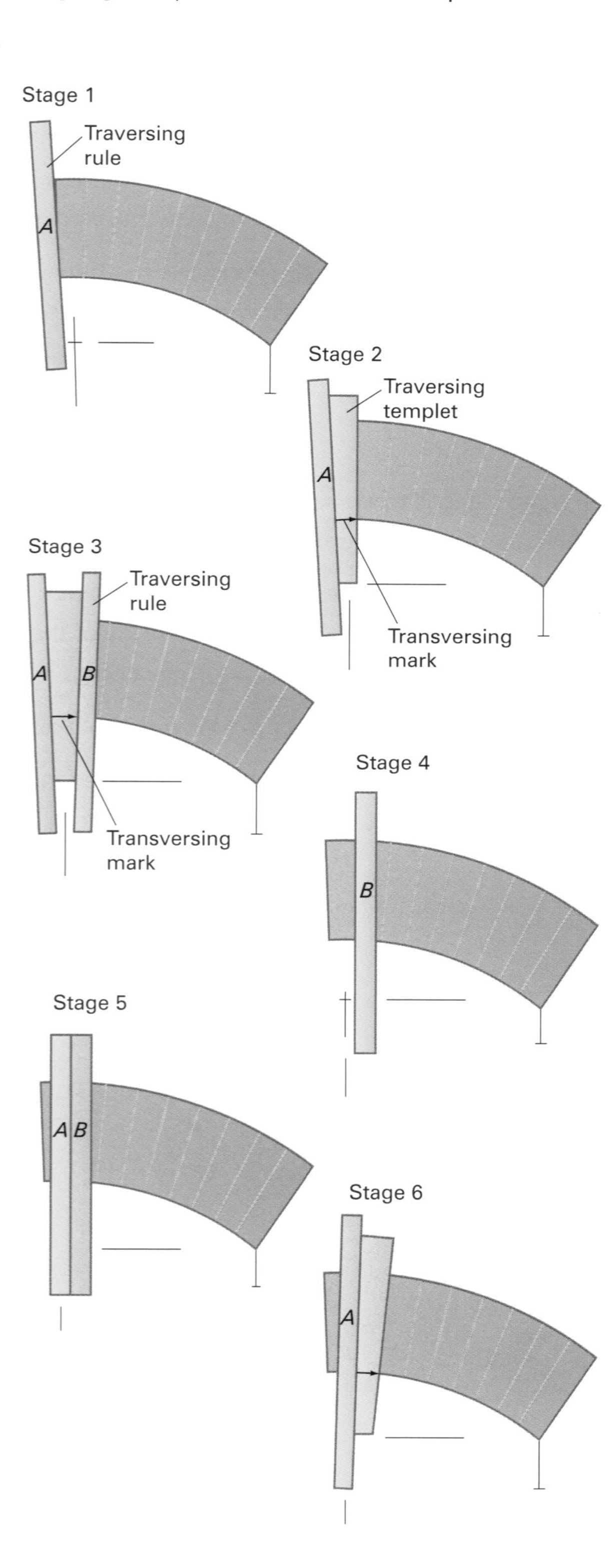

Definition

Traversing – means to go over or trace over the face of the arch with the template to ensure the correct shape has been achieved when producing the template

If the templet reaches the top of the skewback (the extrados) before it reaches the bottom (the intrados), it must be made smaller at the top. If it reaches the bottom before the top, then it must be planed down at the bottom. If there is space left over between the templet edge and the skewback, then the template must be lowered so that the traversing mark is higher up the templet. If it overruns the skewback, then the templet needs to be raised so that the traversing mark is lower down.

Traversing the arch must be repeated until the templet fits exactly between the key and the skewback. This means that the templet will be accurate and the voussoirs cut using it will be the exact shape required to complete the axed arch.

Once the exact shape of the voussoirs has been established, construction of the arch can begin. We have already dealt with the process of setting up the temporary arch support or arch centre in *Brickwork Level 2*.

Having set up the arch centre, the position of the key brick needs to be marked on the face of the arch centre.

The next step is to mark the remaining brick spaces plus one joint either side of the key brick. This can be done accurately with dividers.

The first brick is bedded at the springing point of the arch – you then continue to bed the remaining voussoirs alternately either side of the key brick. This will prevent any unnecessary overloading on either side of the arch centre.

It is important to remember to follow the markings for each brick as the work proceeds.

The arch bricks should be frequently checked for square with a straight edge or alternatively a line should be used across the face of the arch.

Remember

Keep the top of the arch centre free from mortar to prevent unsightly mortar staining on the underneath of the arch bricks once it has been removed.

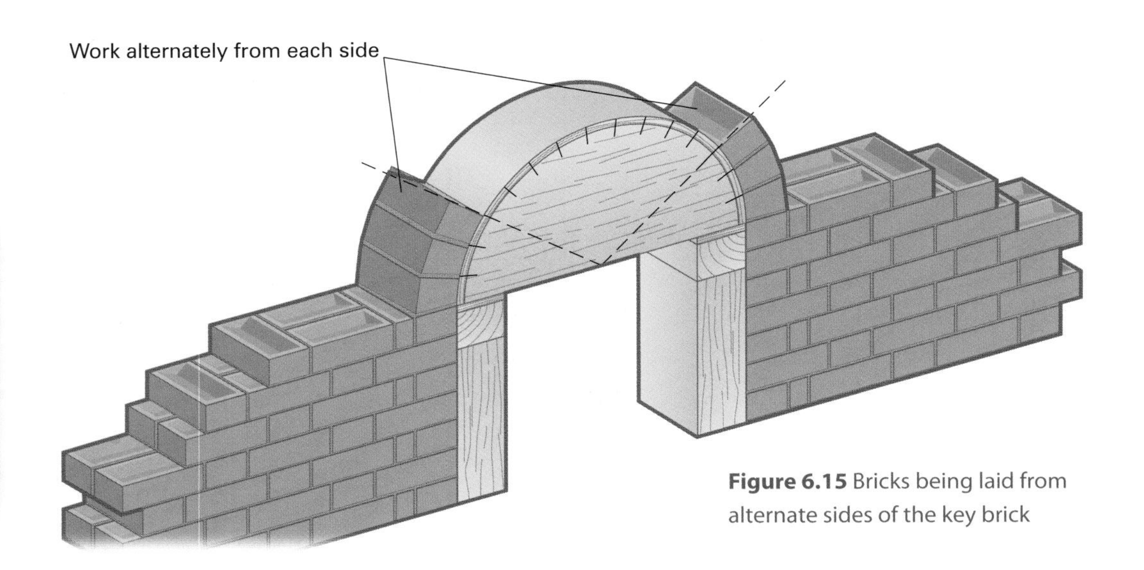

Figure 6.15 Bricks being laid from alternate sides of the key brick

FAQ

Could a piece of string or bricklaying line, fixed at the pivot point, be used instead of a wooden trammel when checking or marking the face of a curved wall either on plan or in elevation?

This is not good practice as there is a possibility that the line may stretch during use giving a false reading, or if the line is not kept taut, again a false reading will be given.

Angled and splayed brickwork

Acute angle – this is an angle less than 90°

Obtuse angle – this is an angle greater than 90°

Not all buildings, boundary walls and garden walls are built with 90° or right angled returns. In some instances it is necessary to build walls at angles to each other in order to follow the lines or boundaries of the site.

Angles at which walls are built other than 90° are known as either acute or obtuse angles.

Where acute or obtuse angles are to be used on site, the angles have normally been established by the architect. In most instances special shaped, purpose-made bricks will be supplied for the construction of angled walls. However it is not uncommon to see acute angles constructed from bricks cut on site. It is highly unlikely that a bricklayer would be expected to cut these angled bricks with normal hand tools as this would undoubtedly result in a large number of wasted bricks. Where these bricks are required to be cut on site, a table saw would be used. It is also important to note that where bricks are cut on site, these bricks should be solid, as bricks with a frog or holes would be virtually impossible to cut to the desired angles.

Acute angles

A number of bonding arrangements for acute angles are shown below.

In walls of 1 brick thickness, acute angles can be produced by bringing the corner of the angled brick structure to a sharp point or alternatively it can be produced by using special shaped bricks which remove the sharp point. Again, the method to be used will be determined by the architect when producing the drawings.

Method 1 – corners produced with a sharp point

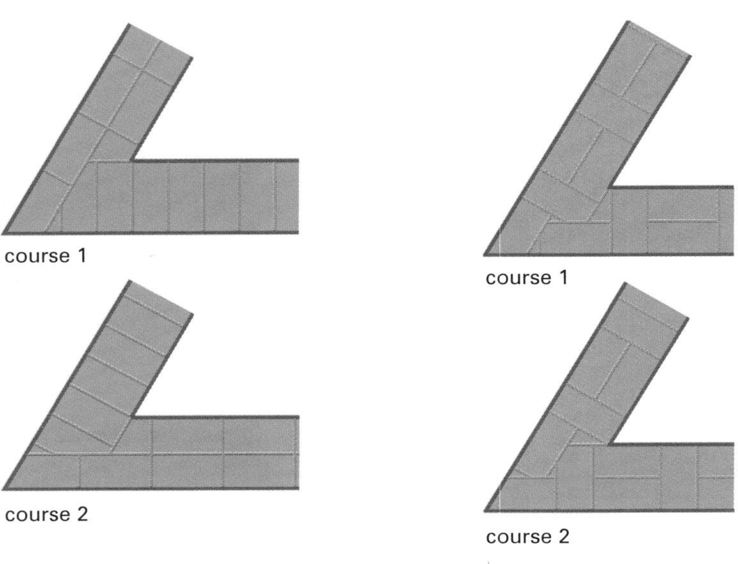

Figure 6.16 Bonding arrangement for 1 brick thick wall in English bond

Figure 6.17 Bonding arrangement for 1 brick thick wall in Flemish bond

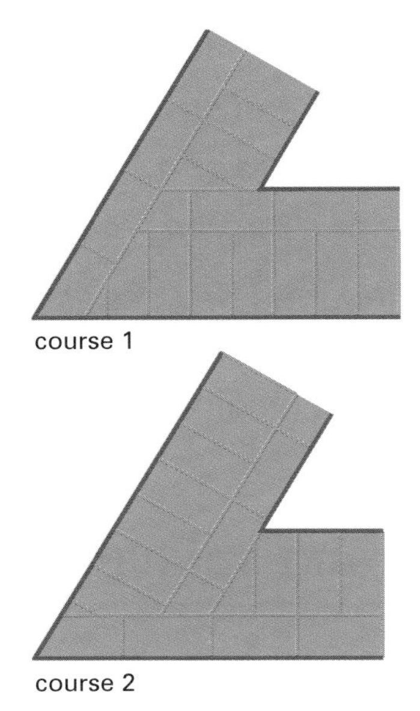

Figure 6.18 Bonding arrangement for 1½ brick thick wall in English bond

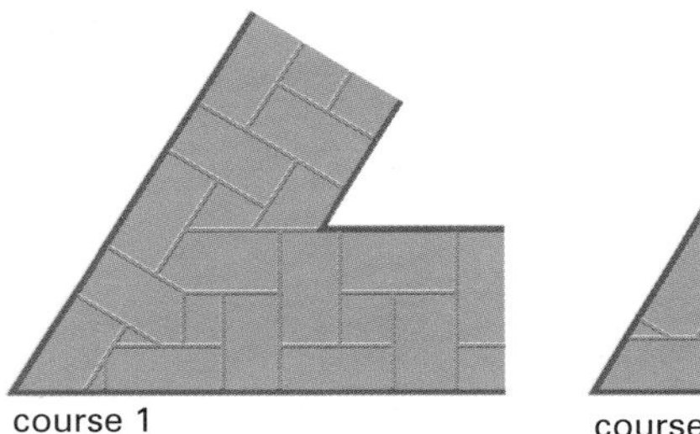

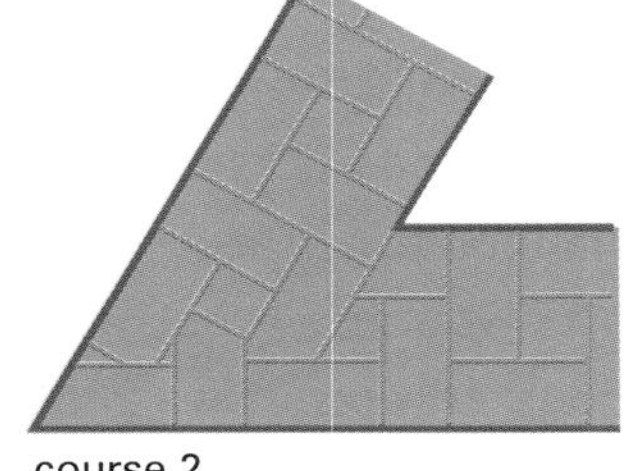

Figure 6.19 Bonding arrangement for 1½ brick thick wall in Flemish bond

Method 2 – special shaped bricks used to avoid sharp point at the corner

Where walls of more than 1 brick in thickness are constructed, a further alternative finish can be provided to the corner. In this method both the sharp point and the use of purpose-made bricks are avoided.

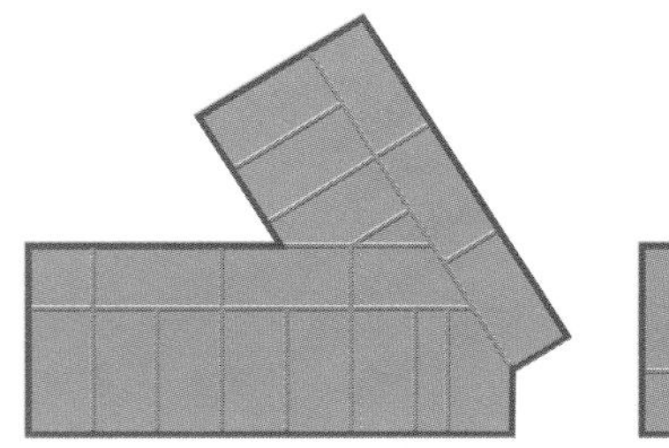

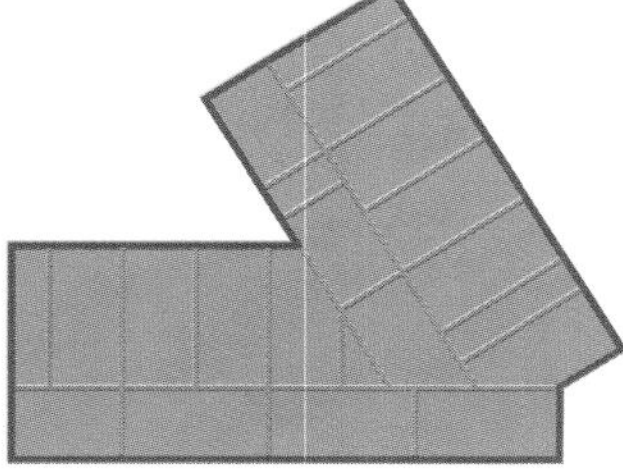

Figure 6.20 Bonding arrangement for 1½ brick thick wall in English bond

External obtuse angles

These types of angles are normally produced using purpose-made bricks known as 'squint' bricks (See Figure 6.35 on page 101). Where angles are required which are not the normal ones covered by the use of squint bricks, then the angles will have to be produced by cutting the bricks on site (again a mechanical table saw will need to be used).

Shown below are a number of bonding arrangements used for producing obtuse angles.

Note

Whenever a squint brick is used at the corner, a closer brick will have to be positioned next to the squint brick in order to produce the correct lap for the bricks along the face of the wall.

course 1
a closer
is placed
next to the
squint brick
course 2

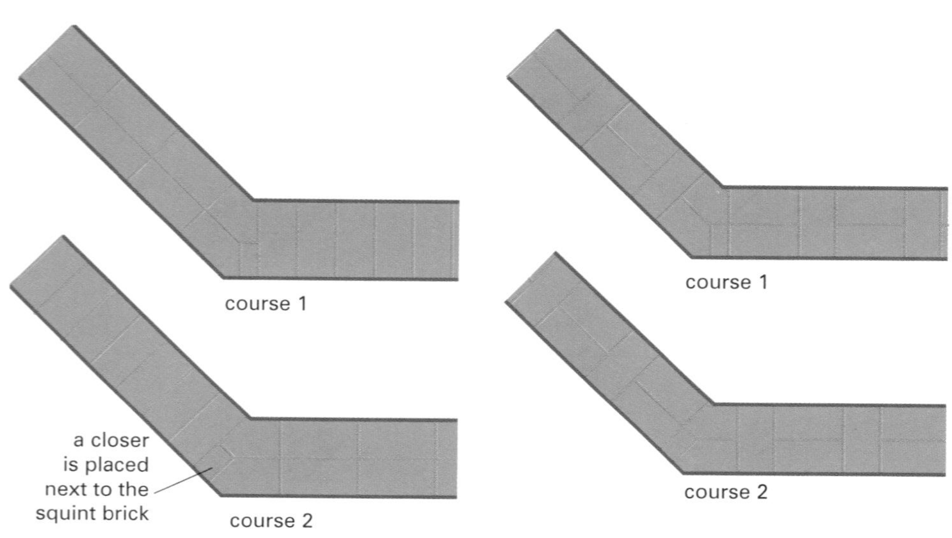

Figure 6.21 Bonding arrangement for 1 brick thick wall in English bond

course 1
course 2

Figure 6.22 Bonding arrangement for 1 brick thick wall in Flemish bond

As with acute angles, an alternative method can be used at the quoin in order to avoid using costly, special shaped bricks.

Definition

Quoin – the corner of a wall

Plan of course 1
Plan of course 2

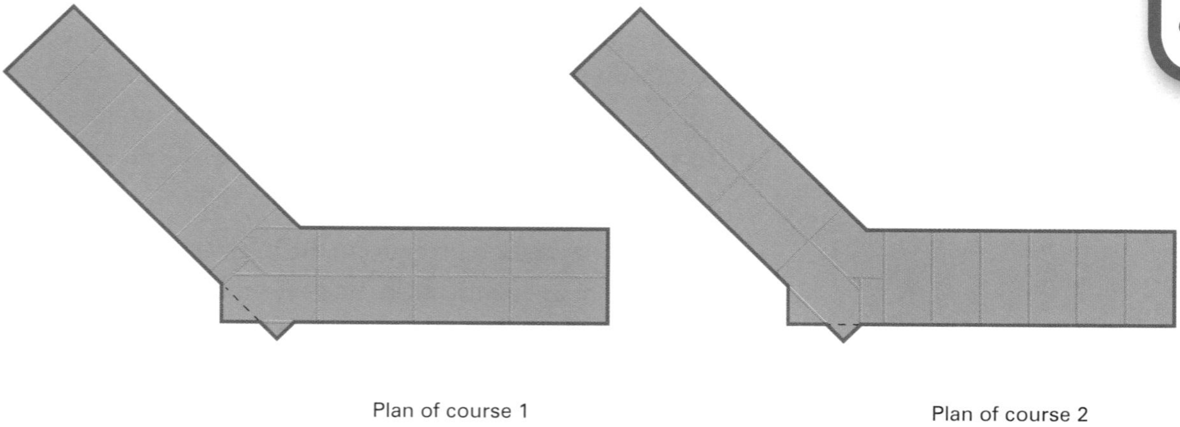

Figure 6.23 Bonding arrangement for the alternative to using squint bricks in a 1 brick thick wall in English bond

Internal obtuse angles

The preferred method of constructing internal obtuse angles is by using a purpose-made brick known as a 'dogleg' (See Figure 6.36 on page 101). The dogleg brick provides a much stronger joint at the intersection of the two lengths of walling.

Using standard, cut bricks can produce a weakness at the intersection of the two walls if the cuts are not accurate and are not lapped correctly.

Shown below are a number of bonding arrangements used for producing internal obtuse angles.

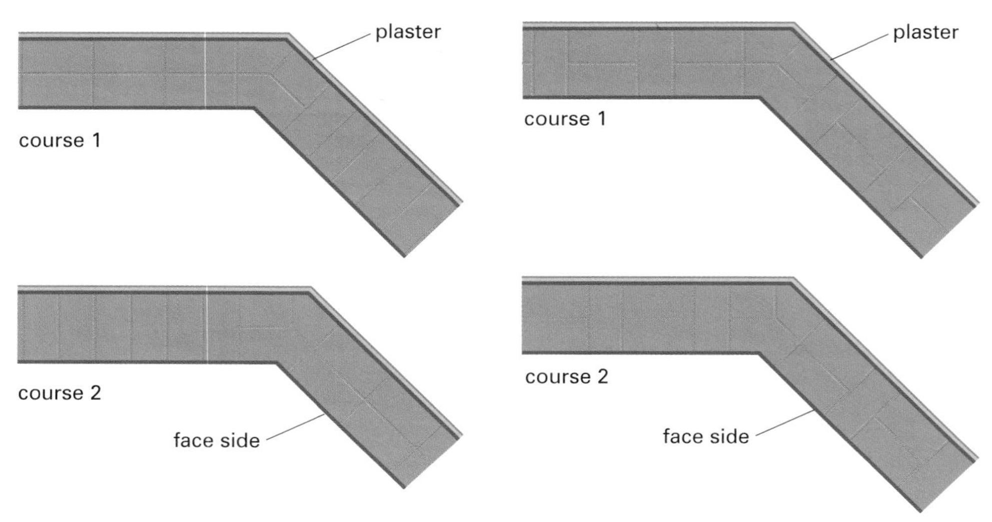

Figure 6.24 Bonding arrangement for 1 brick thick wall in English bond

Figure 6.25 Bonding arrangement for 1 brick thick wall in Flemish bond

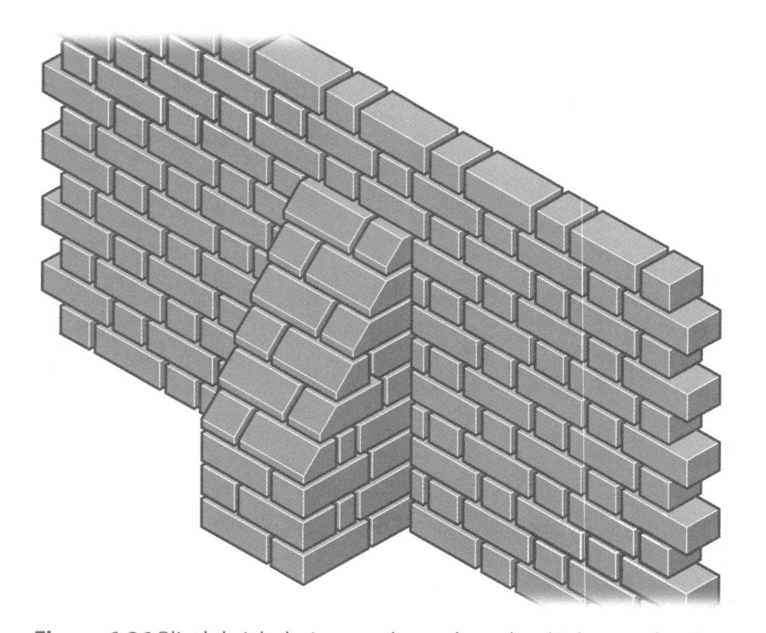

Figure 6.26 Plinth bricks being used to reduce the thickness of a pier

Tumbling-in

Although not commonly seen in modern building projects, tumbling-in was an effective and decorative method of reducing the width of supporting piers or buttresses on retaining or large boundary walls. It was also used in reducing the width of external chimney breasts.

One simple method of reducing the thickness of a wall or pier is to use plinth bricks. However, the face of the angled brickwork is not as appealing to the eye as it is with tumbling-in using standard cut bricks. This is because the face of the work completed with plinth bricks will have small ridges formed by the shape of the plinths.

Method of tumbling-in using standard cut bricks

Where tumbling-in is only required for a short reduction, the angle and cuts can be set out on a large piece of plywood. The angle can then be maintained with the use of a small template cut in the shape of a gun, to the angle required.

For larger reductions where the work cannot be set out on a board, it is necessary to position lines at either side of the tumbling-in. These lines are fixed in place with the use of battens. The positioning of these battens, along with the lines, is shown in Figure 6.28.

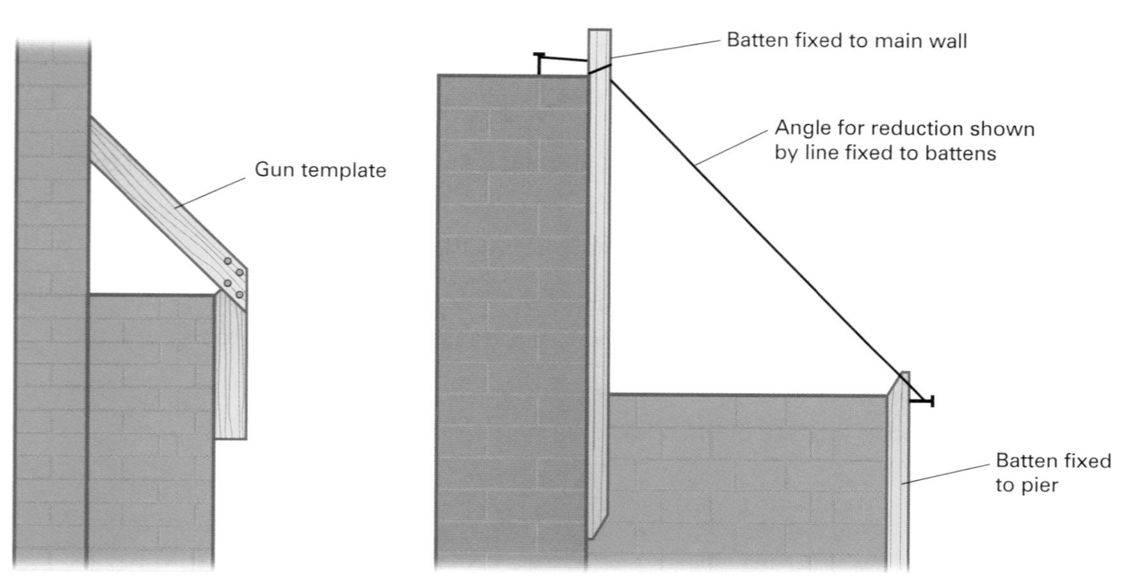

Figure 6.27 'Gun' template used to maintain slope of reduction

Figure 6.28 The position of battens for fixing lines

Once the lines are fixed, a gun template can be made to the angle required and this, as with the previous method described, is used to check and maintain the correct angle throughout the run of tumbling-in.

When starting it is essential that the first course is laid so that it overhangs the brickwork below in order to provide a weathering. This overhang must be provided for when positioning the batten, by extending it past the actual striking point.

It is most important that, as the work proceeds, a gauge rod is used throughout the length of the tumbling-in: failure to maintain gauge would result in unsightly split courses at the top of the tumbling-in.

Where there is a large length of tumbling-in, it is best practice to extend the horizontal brickwork of the pier or buttress to give the impression of both the tumbling-in and the pier brickwork blending into each other. This is shown in Figure 6.29.

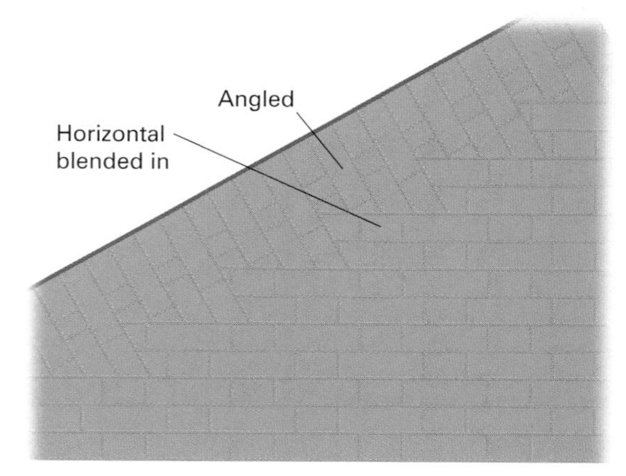

Figure 6.29 A preferred method of blending in the horizontal and angled brickwork

Raking cutting

Gable ends

The most common situation where raking cutting is used is when constructing a gable end.

A typical brick gable end

When constructing a gable end, temporary profiles are required in order to establish the angle of the raking cut and provide a guide for the bricks to be cut. These profiles are in the form of temporary roof trusses or rafters and are positioned immediately behind the wall to be built. The height and pitch of the truss or rafters will have already been determined and this information will be included on the relevant drawings.

A bracket or short length of ridge board is fixed at the top of the profile in order to extend the point of the apex out far enough so that lines can be attached to establish the cutting line.

Once the lines have been set up and the angle of the raking cut has been established, the main walling is constructed and raked back to leave just the spaces for the bricks to be cut.

Temporarily bed the brick to be cut. Mark the brick with a pencil at the points, top and bottom, where the line crosses the face of the brick.

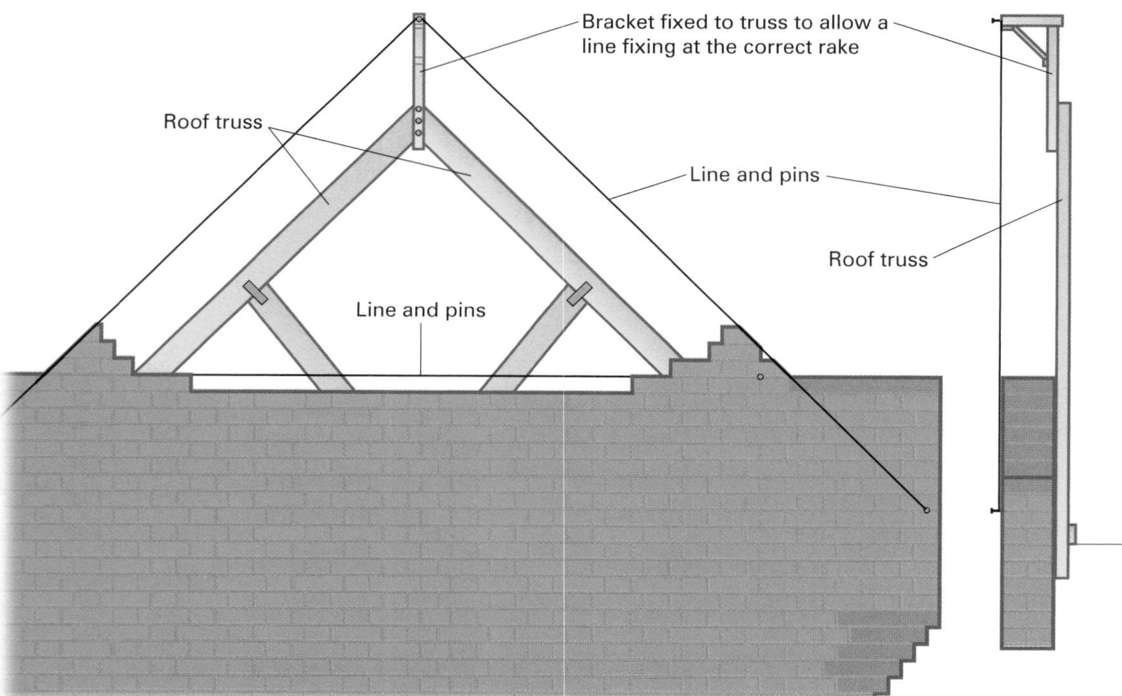

Figure 6.30 The position of temporary profiles (truss/rafters) and lines

Once marked, draw the cutting line across the face of the brick by joining the two previously marked points together. The marking must be transferred to the back face of the brick to ensure that an accurate cut is obtained across the width of the brick.

Trim any excess from the top of the brick using a scutch hammer. Now the brick is ready to be laid to the line.

Special shaped or purpose-made bricks

We have already dealt briefly with a number of special or purpose-made bricks earlier in this chapter - squints, doglegs and plinths. However, there are many variations to these bricks and the number that is actually available is endless and all have their own specific use.

The following is a brief introduction to just some of the special bricks available.

Find Out

Search the websites of leading brick manufacturers to find full details of the varieties of special made bricks currently available

Plinth bricks

These are used to reduce the thickness of walls vertically.

Figure 6.31 A plinth stretcher

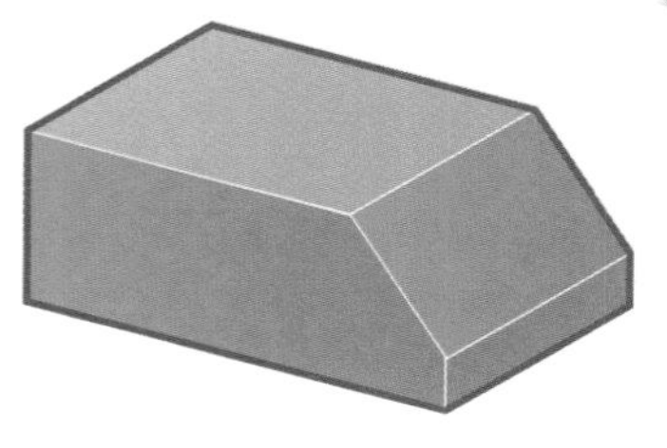

Figure 6.32 A plinth header

Figure 6.33 External plinth return

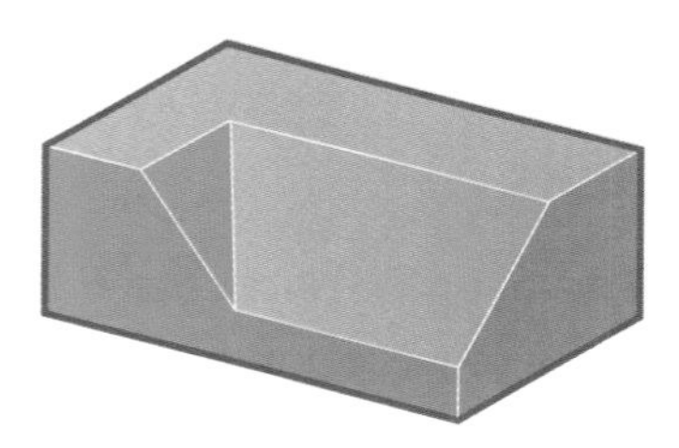

Figure 6.34 Internal plinth return

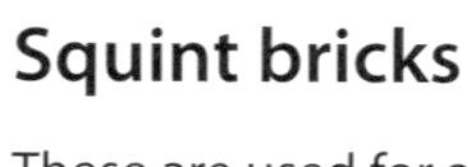

Squint bricks

These are used for acute and obtuse angles.

Figure 6.35 Squint brick

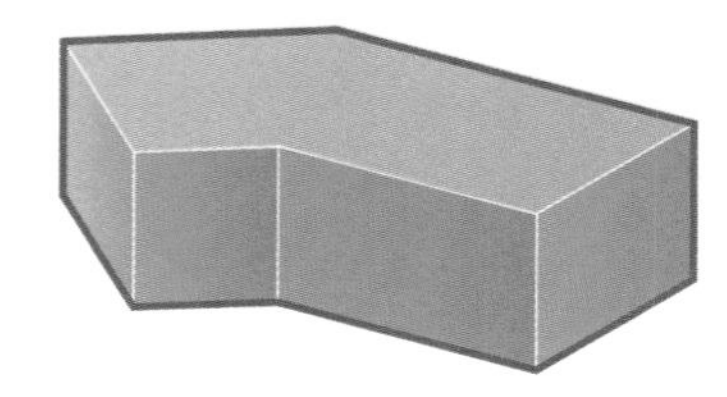

Figure 6.36 Dogleg brick (used for internal angles)

Cant bricks

These are used where corners need to be chamfered.

Figure 6.37 Cant brick

Figure 6.38 Double cant brick

Definition

Cant – meaning bevelled, sloped or tilted

Bull-nose bricks

These are used where the corners need to be rounded.

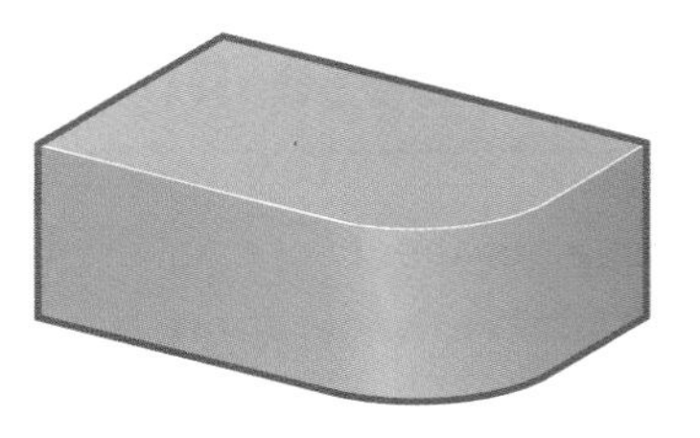

Figure 6.39 Single bull-nose

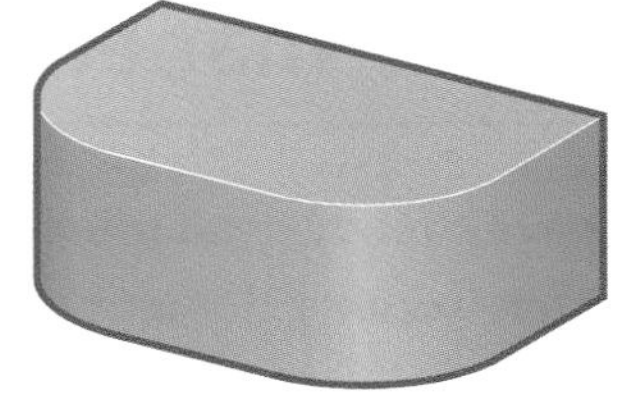

Figure 6.40 Double bull-nose

Capping and coping bricks

These are used to provide a weathering and pleasing finish to the tops of walls.

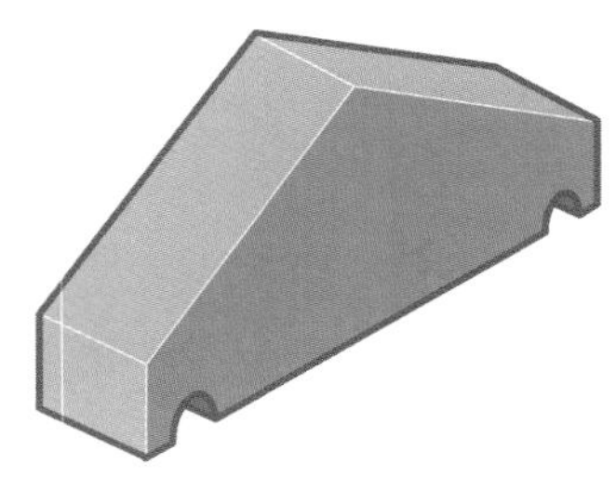

Figure 6.41 Special made brick coping (saddleback)

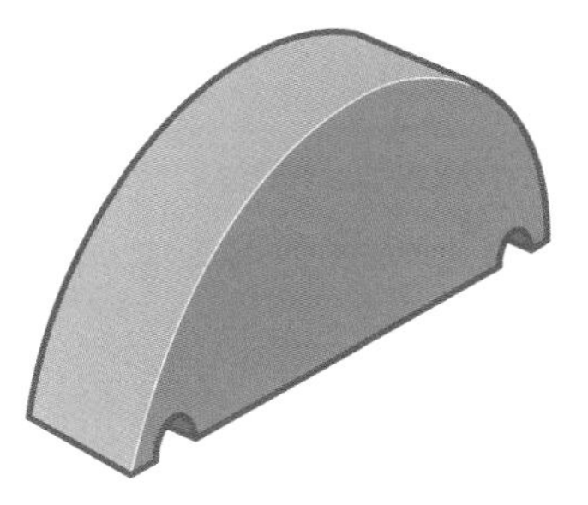

Figure 6.42 Special made brick coping (rounded)

Bonding bricks

These are pre-made standard brick cuts. They are normally made to prevent unnecessary cutting and save on wastage of bricks. These cuts are extremely accurate and are normally used where appearance of the finished article is required to be almost perfect.

Figure 6.43 Half bat

Figure 6.44 Three quarter bat

Figure 6.45 Queen closer

Figure 6.46 King closer

Arch and radial bricks

As the name suggests these are used when constructing feature arches and curved brickwork.

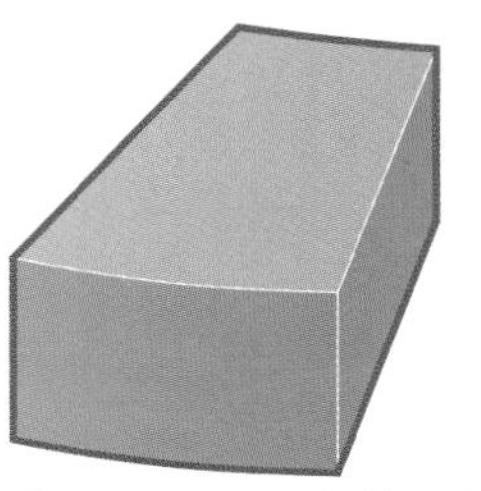

Figure 6.47 Radial brick

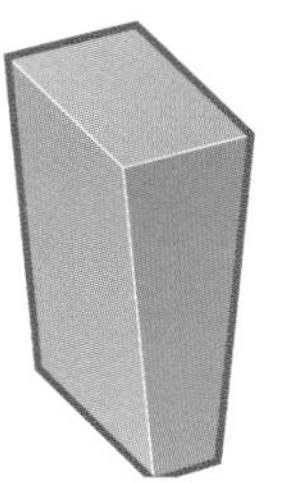

Figure 6.48 Voussoir or arch brick

Slip bricks

These are used where a split course of bricks needs to be introduced into a length of walling.

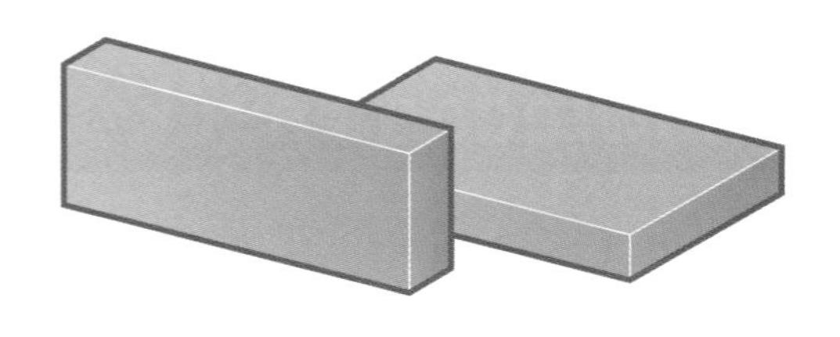

Figure 6.49 Slip bricks

Cill bricks

Again, as the name suggests these are used to form window and door cills.

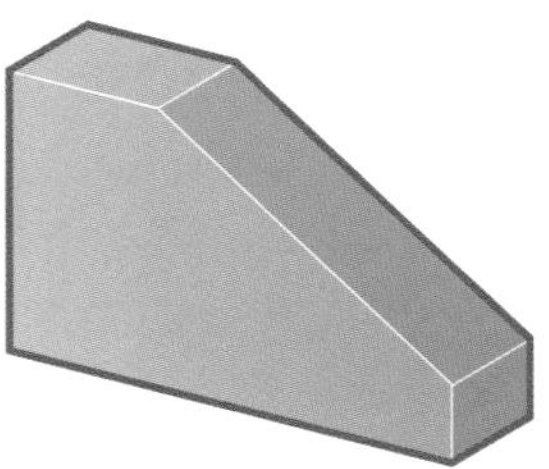

Figure 6.50 Standard cill brick

On the job: Using a mechanical table saw

Joe is a recently qualified bricklayer who is working with a gang of bricklayers. They are constructing a boundary wall with one end finished with a curved ramp feature. Joe has been asked to both mark and cut the bricks for the curve. He has been told that the bricks can only be cut using the mechanical table saw located on site. Although he has been trained and deemed competent in the use of the table saw, he has never been trained in the process of changing a saw blade.

Half way through the cutting job, the saw blade has begun to chip the face of the bricks being cut and is taking longer than normal to cut through the bricks.

What is the possible cause of the bricks becoming damaged and the process taking longer?

How should the problem be rectified and should Joe be the one to carry out any necessary remedial work on the saw?

Knowledge check

1. What is meant by the term 'complex masonry structures'?
2. Explain a 'dog toothing' course.
3. What is meant by the term 'concave curve'?
4. What is an acute angle?
5. What is the name given to the special shaped template used when tumbling-in?
6. What is the most common situation where raking cuts are used?
7. What is meant by a 'serpentine wall'?
8. What type of special made brick would be used for constructing an external obtuse angle?
9. For what purpose would you use a 'dogleg' brick?
10. For what purpose would you use a 'bull-nose' brick?

chapter 7

Fireplaces and flues

OVERVIEW

In the modern era most houses are heated by central heating installations which do not require a fireplace or chimney. However, it is once again becoming very popular to have a fireplace as a feature in a house and in most cases this can be the selling point of a modern day home. Fireplaces consist of a hearth, breast and flue, with a chimney stack to carry the fumes away from the building. This chapter explains the basic requirements and layouts of the fireplace system and gives examples of the different types of fuels used.

This chapter will cover the following:

- The regulations governing fireplace construction
- The different types of fuel used
- Fireplace construction – the different parts that make up the system
- Chimney breast finishes
- Building a chimney stack
- How to fit a hearth and surround.

The regulations governing fireplace construction

The design and construction of fireplaces are controlled by Part J of the Building Regulations as well as guidance and advice being found in the British Standards 6461. The main areas covered are:

- the installation of chimneys and flues for domestic appliances using solid fuels
- BS 1251 specifications for the installation of open-fireplace components
- BS 1181 the specification for liners and terminals
- Part 1 of the codes of practice for chimneys and flues.

These cover the installation in domestic homes for class 1 appliances with an output up to 45 kW. The regulations are mainly concerned with avoiding the spread of fire to the surrounding areas or structures and the release of combustible material into the atmosphere.

The different types of fuel used

In almost every home you will find a fireplace, whether it is used to heat the room it is in, or purely as a feature to give an attractive homely feel. As stated previously, the main design is governed by the Building Regulations. However, the type of fuel used will determine the type of flue required in the construction stage or what needs to be installed if there is a change in the type of fuel used for an existing chimney.

There are four main types of fuel used for heating purposes: solid fuel, gas, oil and electric.

Definition

Open fire - form of heating contained within a fireplace recess

Solid Fuel

Solid fuel is the use of wood or coal, or a combination of both. This is normally in the form of an 'open fire' or it can be a 'wood burning' fire or stove.

Gas

Gas can be used for central heating purposes and with fires connected to chimney breasts.

Oil

Oil is mainly used for central heating purposes; it is very rarely used in conjunction with fireplaces.

Electric

Electricity can be used for central heating. Electric fires can also be fitted to chimney breasts but there is no requirement for a flue as there is no omission of fumes or smoke.

Fireplace construction

A typical fireplace consists of:

- a constructional hearth
- a chimney breast with incorporated flue
- a chimney stack.

Figure 7.1 shows how this fits together and names the different parts involved.

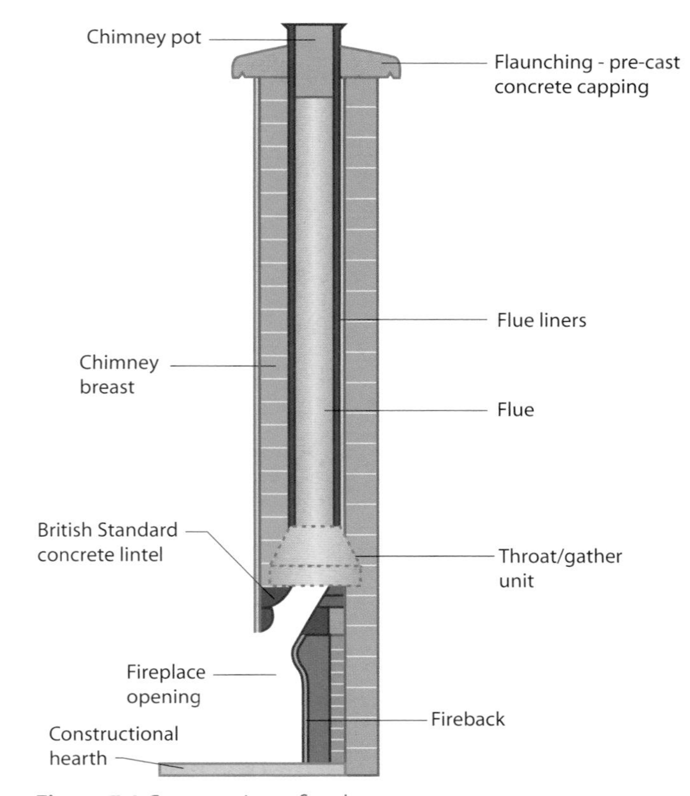

Figure 7.1 Constructing a fireplace

Definitions

There are many names and terms used in the construction of a fireplace. They are listed below so that you can understand their meanings before we go any further.

Chimney breast – projection on a wall which encloses a fireplace or flue

Flue – a channel or duct leading from a fireplace for smoke or fumes to escape

Flue liner– a circular or square liner placed inside a flue to prevent condensation or gases escaping

Constructional hearth – a structural hearth or base under a fireplace to prevent fire spreading

Fireplace opening – The opening that contains the fire or heating appliance

British Standard fireplace lintel - a concrete lintel with a cut out used over fireplace openings

Gather – corbelling of brickwork to reduce a fireplace opening to flue size

Chimney stack – the brickwork above roof level which contains the flue

Necking course – a projecting course of brickwork part way up a chimney stack

Oversailing – the projecting brickwork at the top of a chimney stack for weather protection

Flaunching – the sloping finish to the top of a chimney stack

Chimney pot – the end of the flue very often tapered to accelerate the escape of gases

Flashing – waterproof material (usually lead sheet) used at the joint of a roof and chimney stack

Midfeathers – Brickwork between flues

Class 1 appliance – an appliance not giving an output in excess of 45KW (an open fire)

An external straight cavity wall

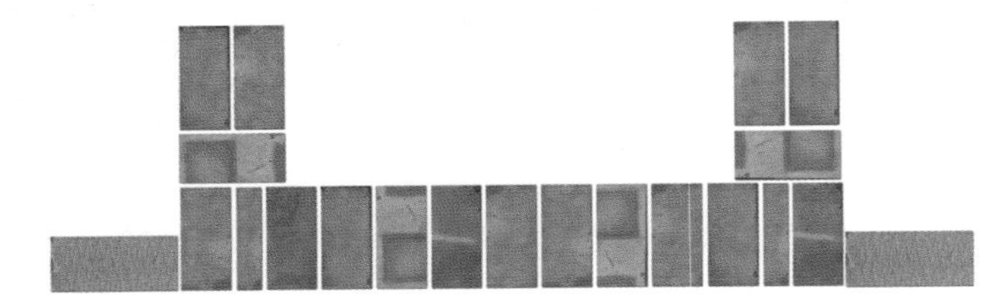

An internal wall

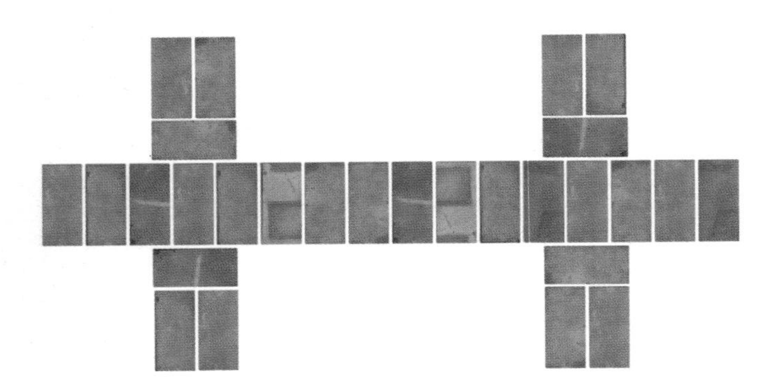

A back to back fireplace

A fireplace should be constructed using a brick wall around its entirety to prevent the spread of fire. This can be done using four main methods that comply with the building regulations:

- In conjunction with an external straight cavity wall.
- With the breast external in a cavity wall.
- In conjunction with an internal wall.
- Built as a double breast, back to back.

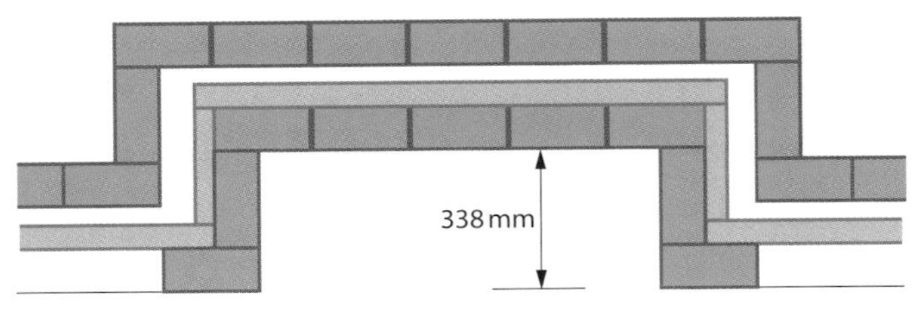

Figure 7.2 The breast external in a cavity wall

More modern or extravagant fireplaces can be built as a corner feature, again using solid brickwork, or circular, self-supporting brickwork, as a central feature to a room.

The constructional hearth

This is a solid base under a fireplace to prevent the spread of fire. It is made of concrete with a minimum thickness of 125 mm. It must extend fully into the depth of the fire opening as well as projecting a minimum of 500 mm in front of the chimney jambs. It is also a requirement to extend a minimum of 150 mm either side of the jambs.

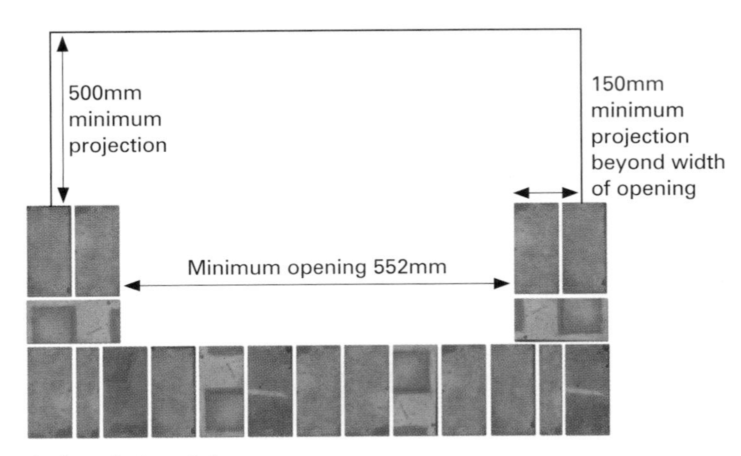

A plan of a hearth base

Building the chimney breast

The sides or jambs of the chimney breast must be a minimum thickness of 1 brick (200 mm) and extend from the back wall by a minimum of 1½ bricks (338 mm). The width of the opening will depend on whether or not a fitted appliance is to be used but the minimum opening size is 2½ bricks (572 mm). This can allow for a change of appliance being fitted at a later date.

The fire opening must be closed at the top to ensure the appliance is fully encased within the chimney breast. This is done by the use of a splayed reinforced concrete lintel to support the brickwork above. This forms the start of the 'throat' of a chimney.

The internal area of the chimney breast now needs to be closed to form the 'flue'. The flue allows the fumes or smoke to escape into the atmosphere. In older properties the flue was made by corbelling the brickwork on both sides on the inside of the chimney breast until the flue size

Note

The opening can be made smaller but it cannot be made bigger at a later date to accommodate a larger appliance. Therefore, if it is not known what type of appliance will be used, it is better at the building stage to have a slightly larger opening

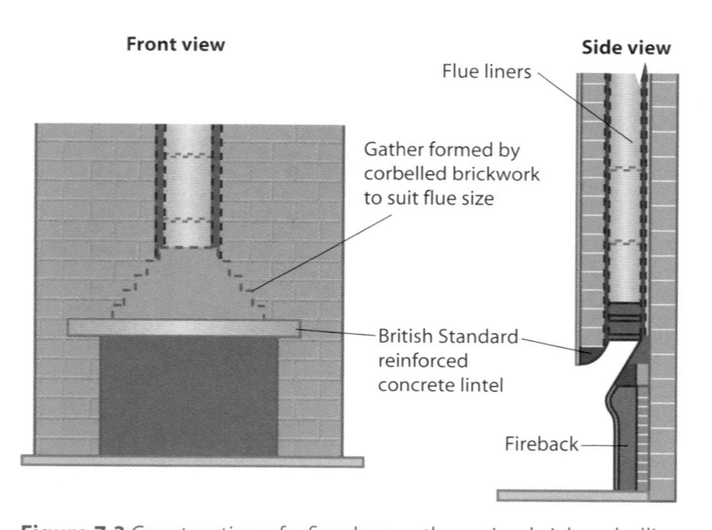

Figure 7.3 Construction of a fireplace gather using brick corbelling

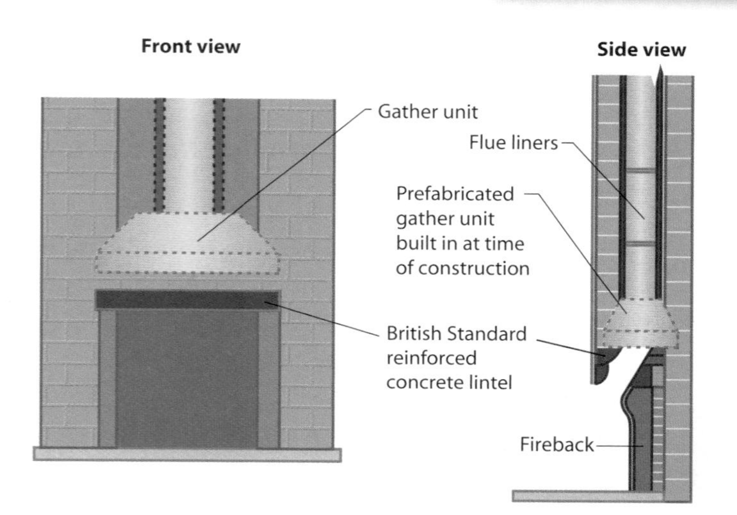

Figure 7.4 Construction of a fireplace gather using a prefabricated unit

(a minimum 215 m square) was reached. This is called the 'gather'. The flue was then corbelled forward on one side and corbelled back on the other, keeping the flue size the same, until reaching the side of the breast. This gave the flue an approximate 45° angle within the chimney to help 'draw' or pull the fumes up into the finished flue. Figure 7.3 illustrates this. Once this was achieved, the flue was then built straight to the top. This could also accommodate a possible fireplace in a first floor room above, meaning the flues would run parallel so that only one double chimney stack would be required at the top.

In more modern homes, a prefabricated unit made from fireproof material (normally concrete) is used (see Figure 7.4). This has the gather incorporated within the unit itself. These come in standard sizes to suit different openings as well as different flue sizes and flue shapes to suit what has been specified.

Flue liners

Flue liners were not really introduced until the 1960s. Up until that point, flues were built square with bricks and the inside of the flue was rendered as it was being built with sand and lime mortar; this was called 'parging' the flue. This was carried out to stop the solid fuel wastes, mainly sulphur, from attacking the bricks. The other problem came from condensation which formed when the hot fumes travelling up the flue met with the cold air from the outside atmosphere. This moisture then ran down the inside of the flue, mixing with the deposited sulphur and forming sulphuric acid and carbonic acid. These could attack the mortar and eventually seep into the bricks and mortar joints. This caused crumbling of the bricks and weakness to the structure, as well as possible staining to internal walls and ceilings. The other problem this could cause is blockage to the flue as a result of parging falling away from the bricks.

The Building Regulations then made the use of liners compulsory to avoid this problem to chimneys in the future.

A typical flue liner

What are flue liners made of?

Flue liners are made from factory manufactured concrete or clay, both of which are non-combustible and resistant to damage by acid attack. They are either round or square and come in various sizes.

How do flue liners fit together?

Flue liners are manufactured with a rebate or socket at one end and a spigot at the other. Thus, when joined to another liner, it forms a perfect seal. These have to be installed the correct way up and the socket/rebated end should always be at the top. This stops any moisture which is

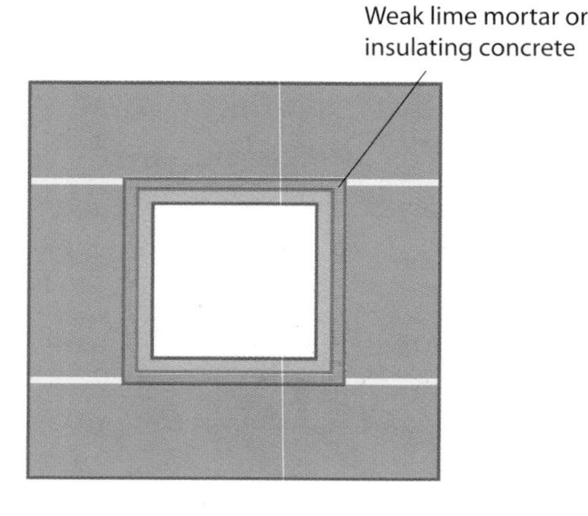

Plan view of chimney stack

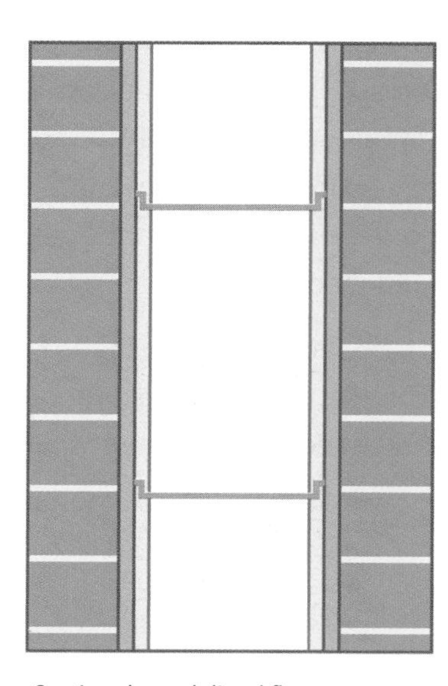

Section through lined flue

Figure 7.5 A section of a flue

running down the inside from penetrating into the surrounding brickwork. The joint between two separate liners should consist of either mortar of the same consistency as the brickwork, or a sulphate resistant mortar, or a manufacturer's sealant.

All liners should be checked for damage and cracks before using them to avoid problems after construction. The area between the outside of the built-in liner and the brickwork should be filled with a material, allowing the liner to expand without causing damage to the liner or surrounding brickwork. This can either be a weak lime/sand mortar or a weak vermiculite concrete mix.

Remember

Make sure joints are left flush in the flue to prevent any obstructions

The finishes to the chimney breast

As we have already noted, the chimney breast at ground floor level is normally the main feature of the room. Therefore, in most modern homes, great thought will go in to the type of finish to complement the fireplace. In the case of open fires which burn solid fuel, some may have 'face' brickwork specifically designed to a customer's specifications across the whole of the breast. Alternatively they may have partial brickwork with a 'mantelpiece' (the rest of the wall having a plaster finish).

Definition

Mantlepiece - a shelf made of wood, tile, stone or brick to finish the top of a fireplace

Stone could also be used as a chimney breast finish, particularly in areas which have plenty of this natural material.

The finished hearth is positioned, normally using the same material (for example, brick or stone). Again, this is for decorative purposes as well as for protection. In the case of an open fire, it is to avoid hot material having contact with the flooring finish.

In the case of gas appliances, where the fire requires specific sealing requirements, other finishes may be used. These can include timber surrounds with marble hearths and 'back panels' in many colours and designs.

Older homes have tiled surrounds and hearths fitted and the fitting would take place after the main structure was built. The fitting of this method will be explained at the end of this chapter. It is a basic method for most fireplace opening finishes (other than structural face brick) but other methods may be used depending on the type of fire to be used.

Note

Great care must be taken to protect the finishes until handover to the client

Fireplace finishes

First floor construction

Once the chimney breast has been built to first floor level, the overall size is reduced to the width of the flue. This is so that it does not take up so much space in the room - it would then have a plastered finish. If a fireplace was to be constructed in the room at first floor level, the construction process would be the same as on the ground floor.

If a chimney breast is built then the reduction will be made at the point the chimney breast reaches the roof space, to start the chimney stack.

Points to remember

- Make sure the foundations for walls meet correct building regulations and specifications.
- Make sure the construction of the brickwork/blockwork is well-bonded and flushed up in accordance with your drawings and specifications.
- Remember the fireplace must contain the fire or appliance and it must also prevent the fire spreading to other parts of the building.
- The flue must be soundly constructed to enable the smoke and gases to be safely carried away to the outside atmosphere without endangering health.
- It must be remembered that fireplaces and flues are hidden behind finished brickwork or plastered walls etc. They are extremely difficult to put right if poorly constructed.

Chimney stacks

A chimney stack is the terminal of the flue or flues. It is very open to the weather so very careful construction is necessary to avoid costly maintenance later. A chimney stack can be very plain or very decorative (this is often seen in older buildings) and can contain one or several flues. The purpose of the stack is the same, whatever the design, and the following points should always be observed.

- As the chimney is one of the most exposed parts of a building, a suitable brick must be used as well as a high standard of workmanship.
- A good chimney pot should be tapered at the top to induce the fumes or smoke to escape and it should be bedded into the brickwork to ensure it is not likely to be moved by high winds.
- A stack must be high enough to clear the roof to discharge the smoke etc safely. It should be at a height that does not affect the health of the occupants or present a fire risk.
- A sound waterproofing of the stack is essential to keep out rainwater.
- The flu liners must carry through to the full height of the stack to meet the chimney pot.

- The joint made by the stack and the roof should be water tight. This is done by what is known as flashing, usually formed in lead sheet by a plumber.
- A DPC should be inserted to prevent moisture passing downwards into the building. Lead sheeting can be used (or engineering bricks as an alternative).

Building the chimney stack

The brickwork and flue should be carried up through the roof space and on to meet the roof. The brickwork should be raised 150 mm or two courses at the front or lowest point of the roof pitch, above the roof.

This is the position where the lead tray should be inserted, to prevent water penetrating down the chimney from saturation of the exposed brickwork above. See Figure 7.6A. The tray should be made of sheet lead and be a minimum of 50 mm wider on each side of the stack size. It should be bedded onto the existing brickwork.

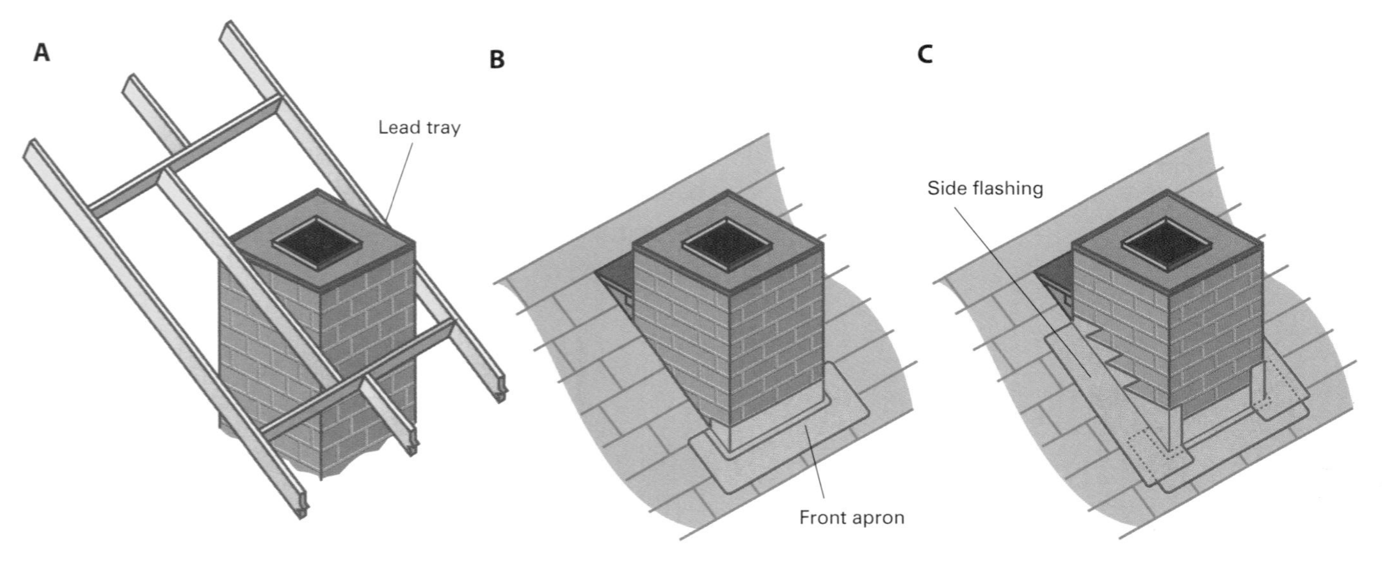

Figure 7.6 Lead positioning on a chimney stack

The flue area is then cut out smaller by a minimum of 25 mm all round; this is so that the lead can be turned up, in order to stop moisture running down the flue.

The brickwork is then continued to form the exposed stack. The joint under the lead at the front and sides outside the roof should be raked out to a depth of approximately 30 mm for future use. Weep holes are installed on the first course above the lead on the exposed front side. The lead overhanging the stack on the outside should be turned up tight to the stack but, where it is inside the roof, the overhang should be turned down on the front and side areas above the rafter line after the front apron is fitted. This is to force any water that penetrates the stack to run out at the front of the chimney through the weep holes situated in the perp joints. See Figure 7.6B.

The brick joints should be raked out in readiness for the lead flashings to be inserted in order to waterproof the sides and back as the stack is built. See Figure 7.6C.

Note

If you are unsure of the exact position, rake out more than is required. It is easier to re-point than to have to cut out hardened joints at a later date when there is a chance of stack damage

Stack on ridge or no more than 600 mm from it. Must be a minimum of 600 mm

600 mm

600 mm

Minimum height of stack 2300 mm or less from rooflight 1000 mm

rooflight

1000 mm

2300 mm

Stack 1000 mm minimum above roof level

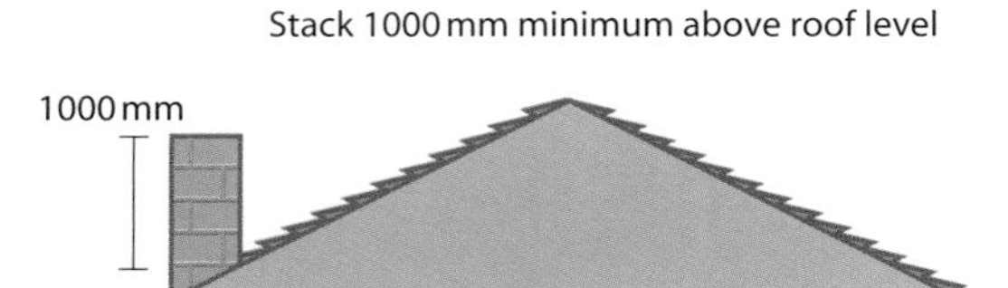

Figure 7.7 Regulated heights of chimney stacks

Once the brickwork has reached a height of 150 mm (two courses) above the roof at the back, a second DPC tray can be fitted and the joint raked out to take the back lead apron. (This is the same operation that was previously carried out with the front apron to prevent water penetration.)

The stack is then built up to the height specified or to Building Regulation heights as shown in Figure 7.7, allowing for oversail courses to be built.

Oversail courses

Oversailing is the projecting brickwork at the top of a chimney stack which helps to protect the stack from the elements. A minimum of one course is set out overhanging the stack on all sides. The remaining course or courses, depending on the feature at the top, are then completed and the chimney pot is incorporated.

The top is then sealed with mortar raised at the pot edges to allow water to run away from the top. This is called 'flaunching'. The water will then run off the top and past the chimney stack and not down its length.

An alternative finish to the top would be a purpose-made capping made of concrete that is bedded on. It has a central hole to allow the pot or liner to pass through to the required height; this would then be sealed with mortar between the pot and capping.

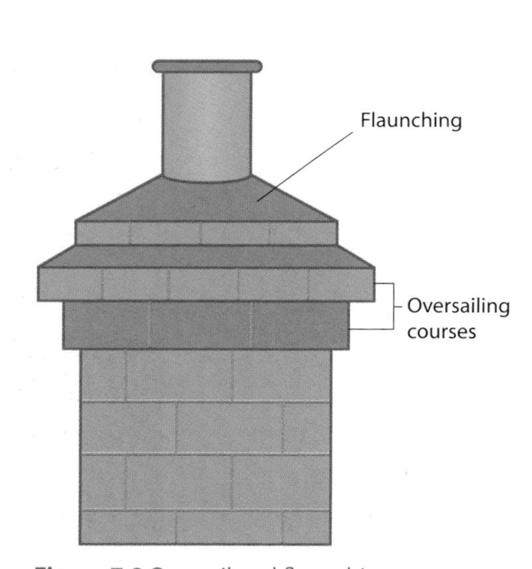

Figure 7.8 Oversail and flaunching

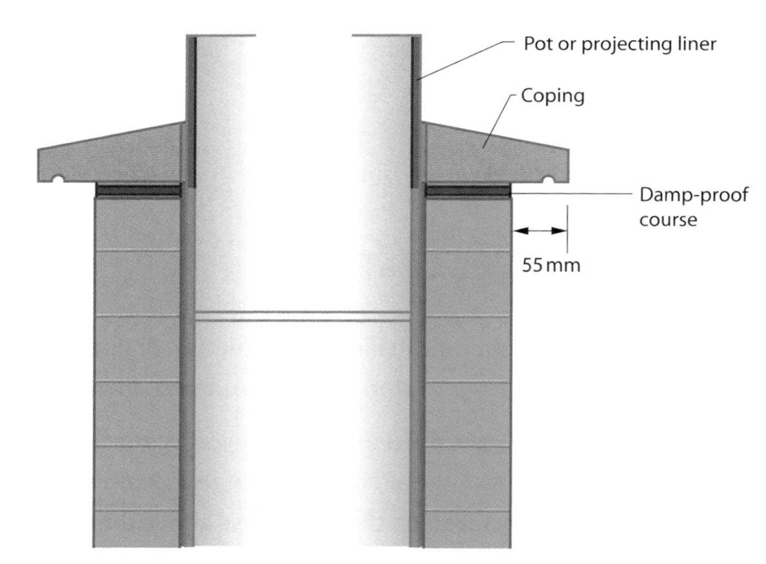

Figure 7.9 Concrete capping finish

The fitting of a hearth and surround

As we have already said, the surround and hearth are fitted after the main construction has taken place. At this point in the construction process, unless the internal brickwork is to be 'faced', the internal opening needs to be finished to take the required appliance.

Fitting the fireplace

Stage 1

The first stage is to position the surround close to the opening to avoid excessive lifting, but be careful not to damage the edges of the surround or finished decoration. Measure the chimney breast and mark a centre line with a pencil or a cut line in cement screed. Measure and put a small mark on the centre of the surround on the top edge with a pencil but be careful not to scratch it or use a marker that cannot be wiped off easily or the surround will be permanently damaged.

Stage 1 Positioning the surround

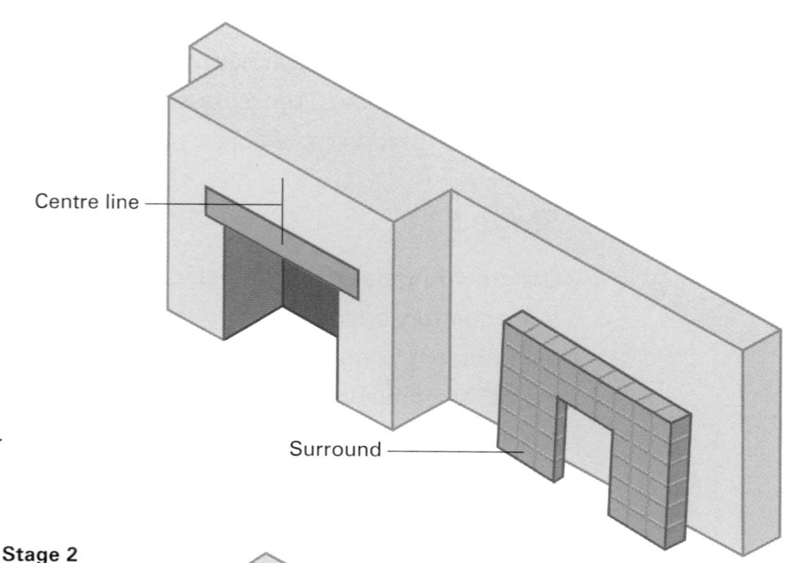

Stage 2

The back hearth within the fireplace opening has to be raised to the thickness of the hearth to allow it to take the fireback. This can be done by using split bricks and then covering with a thickness of sand/lime mortar, or fully with mortar, making sure the finish is level both ways. In some instances firebricks may be used as the finished back hearth.

Stage 2
Fixing the back hearth

Centre line

Raised back hearth

Stage 3

Lift the fireback into place within the opening and set central to the line marked on wall.

Stage 3
Fixing the fireback

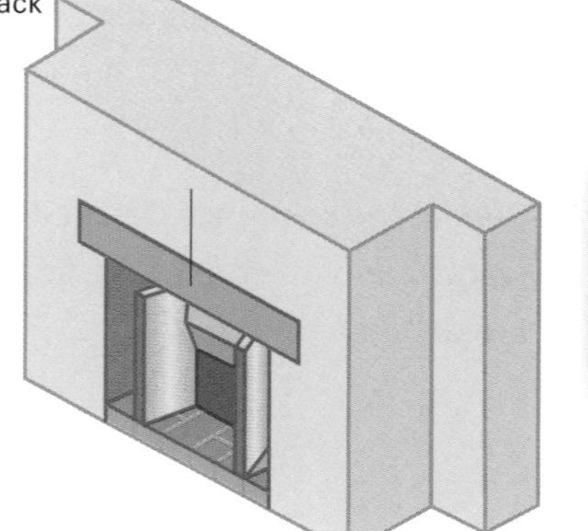

Figure 7.10 The stages of fitting the hearth and surround

Note

If the wall has been finish plastered, the area of the fixing lugs should be cut out with a hammer and chisel to allow the fixing to be covered at completion

Note

It is advisable that the rope is one continuous section

Stage 4

Reposition the surround and line up the two centre lines. Check and make sure it is level and plumb on the face side. Move the fireback so it is positioned almost against the surround (leaving a gap of approximately 25 mm to allow for the expansion rope). Mark the positions of the fixing plugs on the surround onto the chimney breast wall ready for drilling. Then remove the surround to its resting position.

Stage 4 Checking the position of the fireback

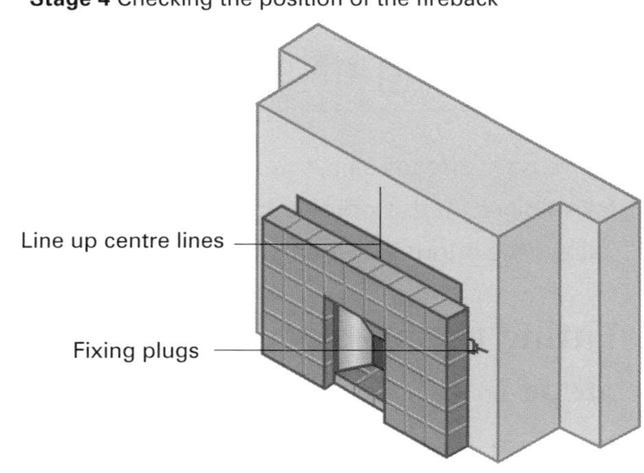

Stage 5

Drill the fixing holes using an electric drill or battery operated drill to take red or brown fixing plugs, making sure the depth of the holes are correct. A minimum size of 50 mm screw should be used.

Stage 5 Drilling the fixing holes

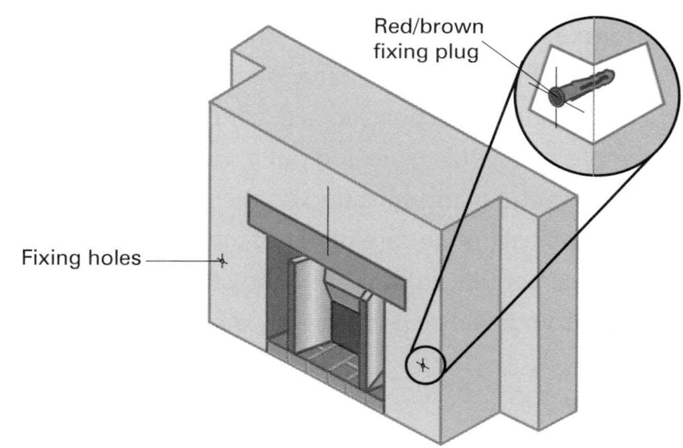

Stage 6

The next stage is to build in the fireback. Corrugated paper should be positioned around the rear of the fireback to allow for any expansion while in use. The gaps on each side should be filled first with bedded bricks or cut bricks to stop any overspill. The void at the back should then be filled with lightweight vermiculite concrete or sand lime mortar but make sure if mortar is used it does not push the fireback forward under the pressure.

Stage 6 Building in around the fireback

Stage 7

Repeat the sequence detailed in stage 6 until the top of the fireback is reached.

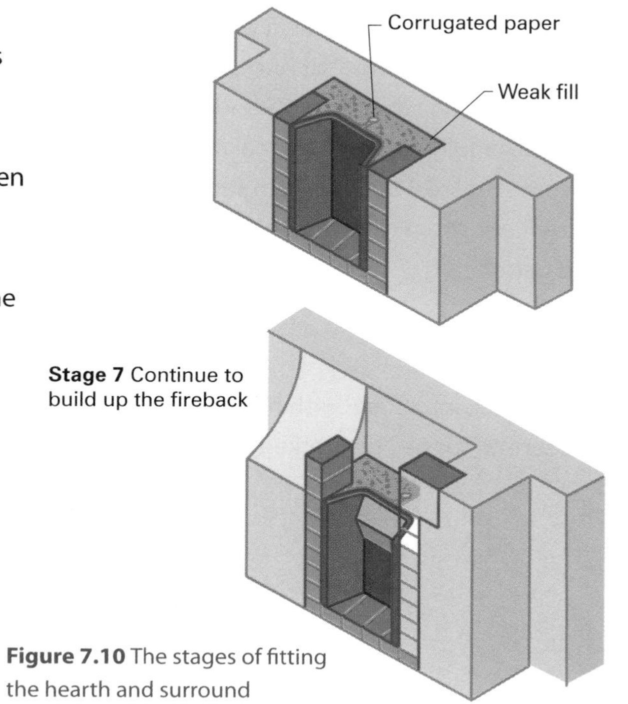

Stage 7 Continue to build up the fireback

Figure 7.10 The stages of fitting the hearth and surround

Stage 8

The space between the top of the fireback and the back wall, a distance of about 100 mm, should now be filled with sand/lime mortar at an angle of approximately 45° to give maximum draw for the smoke and gases to escape.

Stage 9

Lift the surround into position and line up the centre marks and fixings, level and plumb in position. Next, fit the fire resistant rope into the gap along both sides between the fire back and the surround and across the top between the surround and chimney breast, making sure it is approximately 25 mm behind the face line. Then position the screws into the lugs and tighten until fully secured.

Stage 10

Bed the hearth into position ensuring it is level both ways and point the gap where the rope is fitted with fire cement to ensure a seal between the surround and fire back. The chimney breast should now be plastered or if this has been carried out, the gap sealed with mastic. Clean off the surround to remove any excess material and protect with paper or bubble wrap on completion.

Please note:
Stages 9 and 10 may be done in reverse order depending on the type of hearth used. When stage 10 is carried out first, the bedded hearth must be fully dry to take the weight of the surround.

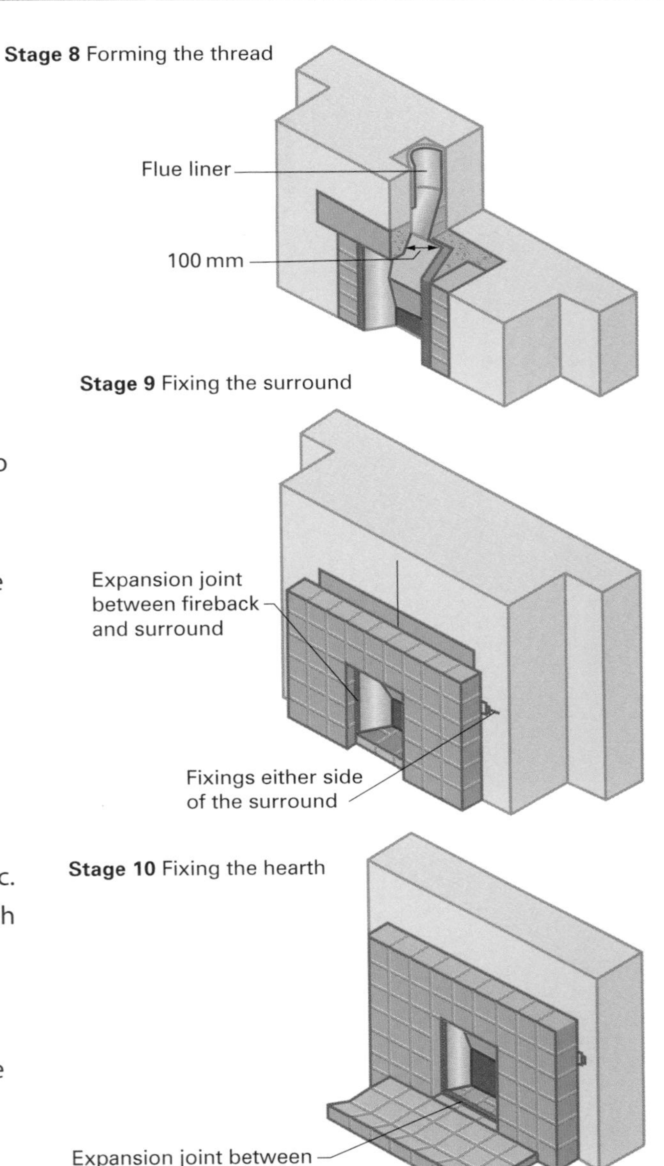

Figure 7.10 The stages of fitting the hearth and surround

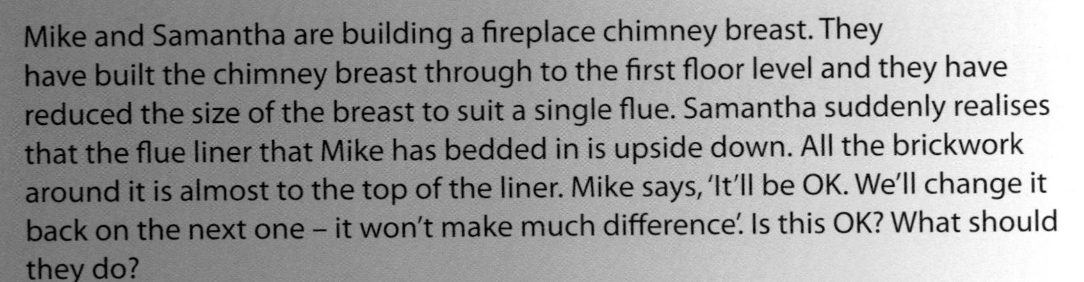

On the job: Building a chimney breast

Mike and Samantha are building a fireplace chimney breast. They have built the chimney breast through to the first floor level and they have reduced the size of the breast to suit a single flue. Samantha suddenly realises that the flue liner that Mike has bedded in is upside down. All the brickwork around it is almost to the top of the liner. Mike says, 'It'll be OK. We'll change it back on the next one – it won't make much difference'. Is this OK? What should they do?

FAQ

What happens if the fireplace finish has not been decided and I obviously have to build the chimney breast to tie into the structural wall as I go?

This is not a problem. Build as normal and if there is a chance that a full or part brick fireplace may be built, wall ties should be built into the breast and left to tie in the new breast. If this doesn't happen they can be cut off at a later date and plastered over. Just make sure you put in enough ties to start with.

Knowledge check

1. What is the constructional hearth for?
2. What are flashings used for?
3. What is a chimney stack?
4. What is classed as solid fuel?
5. What is flaunching?
6. What are the four main types of fuel used for heating?
7. What materials are flue liners made of?
8. What is gathering?
9. Where is a pot positioned?
10. What is a Class 1 appliance?
11. What part of the Building Regulations covers chimney work?
12. What is the minimum thickness of chimney jambs?

chapter 8

Erecting masonry cladding

OVERVIEW

With the introduction of both timber and steel framed structures into modern day construction projects, cladding has become the ideal way of transforming these types of potentially drab and dreary buildings into structures which fully complement the aesthetic requirements of the environment in which they are built.

This chapter will cover the following:

- types of cladding
- methods of supporting/fixing cladding.

Definition

Load-bearing - walls referred to as load-bearing support the load from roofs and floors

Introduction

Traditional construction methods require the bricklayer to build outer and inner leaves of brick and block work with a gap separating them which is between 50 and 75 mm. The two separate leaves are tied together using galvanised steel ties. This is referred to as cavity wall construction. In most cases cavity walls built in the traditional way are **load-bearing**. However, the traditional cavity walling construction is usually restricted to buildings of no more than two or three storeys in height.

For information on methods of constructing cavity walls, refer to *Brickwork Level 2*, Chapter 12.

Where buildings are built in excess of three or four storeys an outer skin of facing brickwork may be used to cover the main framed structure. Traditionally, these multi-storey buildings were constructed from pre-cast concrete sections slotted together. This outer skin will be tied in to the main structure using purpose made fixings or metal support systems. A cavity will still need to be formed to ensure that the correct insulation properties required for the building are achieved. In most instances the outer skin will not be required to carry any loads imposed by floors or roofs as these loads will be supported by the main framed structure.

Where the brick outer skin is not required to support any load, it is known as masonry cladding.

Note

The main purpose or function of any masonry cladding is to provide the decorative finish to a structure

Masonry cladding is also used to cover buildings of timber frame and steel framed construction. Timber frame construction is becoming increasingly more popular in modern day house building. The inner leaf of timber frame buildings consists of pre-formed panels made from structural timbers which are capable of supporting the loads imposed by the floors and roof. Steel framed structures are more commonly used for buildings such as factory and warehouse units. As with the more traditional multi-storey concrete structures, the cladding will be tied back to the main structure with the aid of metal support systems.

In whatever situation masonry cladding is used there are a number of different methods of installing and fixing the cladding to the main structure. This chapter will deal with the more common methods and fixing systems used. There are a wide variety of fixing systems available in today's market place and it is impossible to cover all of them.

Note

Whichever system is used in a building project, full installation guidance will be provided by the manufacturers

Below we will cover the following in relation to masonry cladding:

- types of cladding
- methods of supporting/fixing cladding.

Types of cladding

Although this chapter will deal specifically with masonry cladding there are a number of materials other than brick and block which can be used to clad a structure. The most common types of cladding used in modern day construction are described below.

Traditional brick and block cladding

This type of cladding consists of an outer leaf of brick or block being constructed using the normal materials and methods associated with building cavity walling. It is tied back to the main structure using specially designed ties. However, as we have already stated, this method of cladding is restricted to low rise buildings of no more than two or three storeys. This is because walls constructed in this way are incapable of adequately self supporting their own weight when certain heights are exceeded. Other properties are also affected when using this method for taller buildings, such as movement due to shrinkage of the main structural components, stress to the structure caused through wind pressures, settlement within the main structure, etc.

Pre-cast brick panels

These units are pre-cast and manufactured in production plants away from the construction site where they are to be used. These pre-cast panels are usually much thinner in section than traditional brick outer leaves and are fixed back to the main structure or to themselves. There are numerous cladding systems of this type available and each is fixed in its own special way. In many instances these types of cladding systems are fixed in such a way that the need for traditional mortar courses and jointing methods is removed. This type of cladding is not designed to carry any structural loads.

In addition to the pre-cast units already mentioned, there are an increasing number of examples where pre-fabricated brickwork is being used in modern construction projects. Pre-fabricated brickwork consists of panels of traditional brickwork being built in a production plant and transported to site where it is lifted into position. This type of design requires the brickwork to be pre-tensioned with the use of steel reinforcement so that the whole panel can be transported from the factory to the site without damaging or weakening the brickwork.

An example of pre-cast cladding panels

Note

This type of cladding is mainly used on steel or concrete framed structures

Brick slip and brick tile systems

This type of cladding consists of **brick slips** or tiles of approximately 25 mm–35 mm in thickness fixed to a pre-fabricated panel which is in turn fixed to the main structure.

The slips or tiles are fixed either by using a special adhesive or by mechanical fixing methods. All joint finishing is normally carried out once the installation is complete. Joint finishing is achieved by pumping a special cement based mortar into the vertical and horizontal joints and then forming a joint finish in the normal way.

Definition

Brick slips - these usually have the same dimensions in relation to length and height as the standard clay bricks used in traditional construction methods. However, the thickness of the slip is normally no more than 25 mm. Generally brick slips are made from exactly the same material as the standard clay bricks

Alternative cladding materials

In addition to the brick and block type claddings, pre-cast panels can also be produced from materials such as concrete, stone, granite and slate.

Of the alternative cladding materials, concrete cladding is the most common. This type of cladding is normally in the form of pre-cast concrete panels which are reinforced with steel mesh and/or rods. They are available in a wide range of colours and finishes. The finish of these units can be formed to resemble a stone effect, standard rendered finishes and even a brick effect facing.

Methods of supporting/fixing cladding

As previously mentioned, there are many new cladding systems being introduced into construction and each has their own particular installation procedures and fixing components. It is impossible to cover all of these within this chapter. However, the following section will provide you with an insight into both traditional methods of installing and fixing different types of cladding and the basic principles behind the more modern methods.

Did you know

Some manufacturers of brick slips and tiles are now producing this type of cladding in sizes larger than the standard brick sizes

Whichever support system is used when installing cladding, it is of the utmost importance that the installation procedures are accurately followed. Failure to follow guidelines may result in failure of the support system and eventual weakening of the cladding sections and in some instances even collapse.

Traditionally, brickwork cladding used on multi-storey concrete structures is supported at each floor level by specially formed and reinforced concrete toe or edge beams. These toe or edge beams are formed as part of the concrete floor slab.

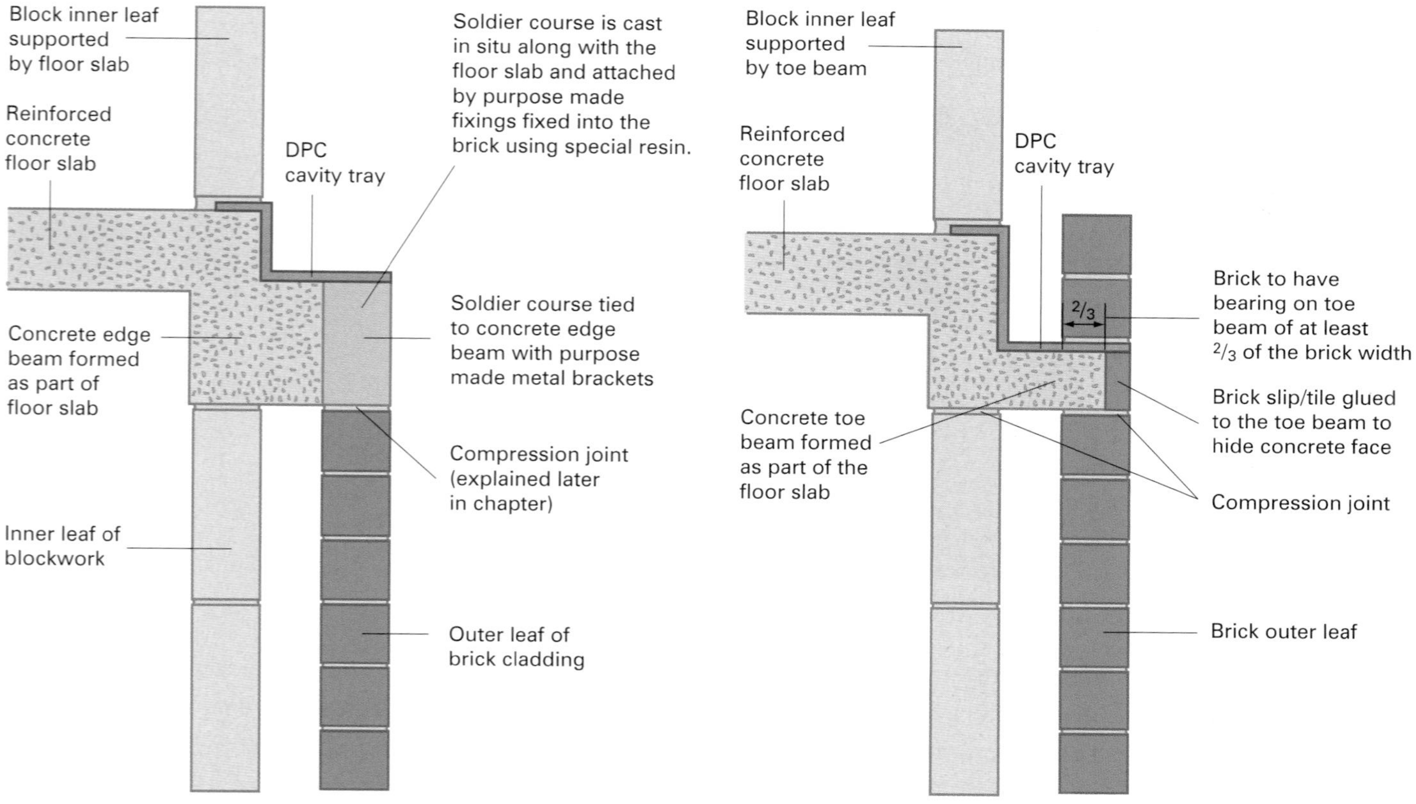

Figure 8.1 Typical concrete floor slab incorporating a reinforced edge beam

Figure 8.2 Typical concrete floor slab incorporating a reinforced toe beam

With the introduction of metal support systems the use of concrete support beams is becoming less common.

Continuous lengths of metal supporting beams can be fixed to the structural concrete by either purpose made expansion bolts or by specially designed bolts which fit into a channel slotted in or fixed to the surface of the concrete.

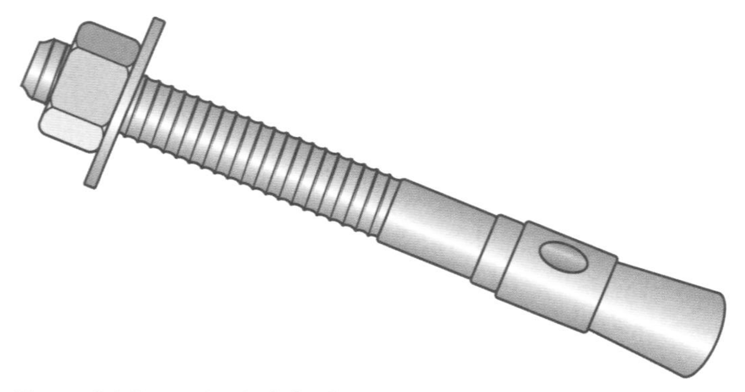

Figure 8.3 Expansion bolt for fixing a support beam to a concrete structure

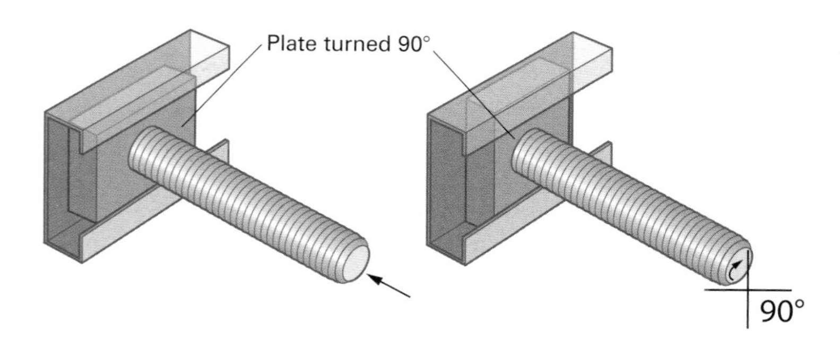

Figure 8.4 Purpose made bolts slotting into a channel fixed to the main concrete structure

When fixing these types of metal supports to steel framed structures the support beam can be fixed directly to the steel frame without the need to use additional channelled fixing supports.

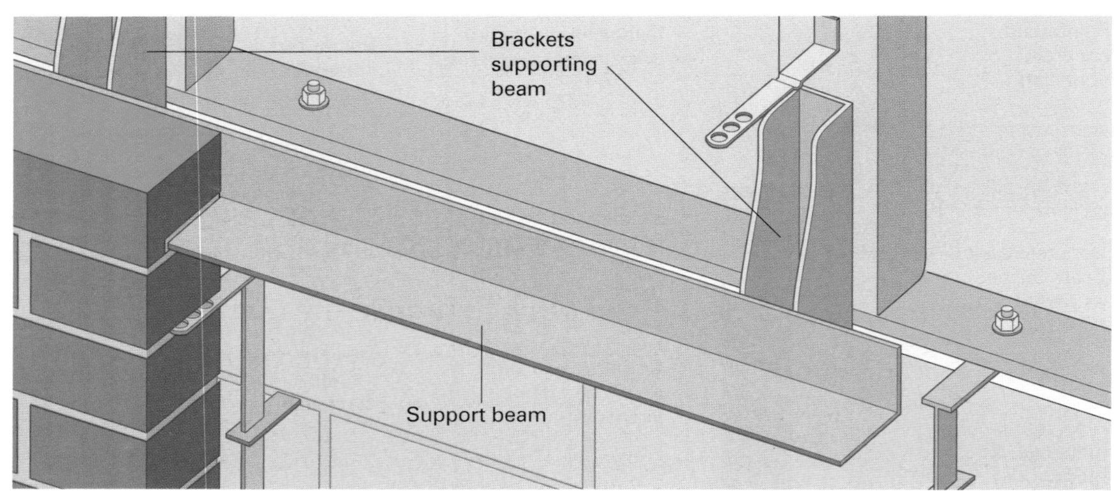

Figure 8.5 Support beam attached directly to a steel frame

In most instances, brickwork cladding will be supported at each floor level when using the metal support systems. In addition to the metal supports, horizontal movement joints need to be incorporated. This is also the case when brick cladding is supported by concrete toe or edge beams. These movement joints are of vital importance in order to allow for shrinkage or expansion, over time, of various materials such as concrete or brickwork.

The horizontal movement joint is to be provided between the underside of the metal angle and the course of brick beneath the angle (see Figures 8.1 and 8.2). The movement joint should be totally free from mortar. A special compressible strip or filler is used to replace the mortar. In order to ensure water or moisture does not penetrate through this joint into the inner leaf, the filler or compression strip is set back from the face of the cladding by approx 10–15 mm - this space is then filled with a waterproof, compressive sealant.

Did you know

Horizontal movement joints are referred to as compression joints

The thickness of the metal support beam will be determined by the amount or weight of the brickwork cladding to be supported. Obviously the thicker the supporting beam is, the thicker the joint will be between the brickwork cladding above and below the beam.

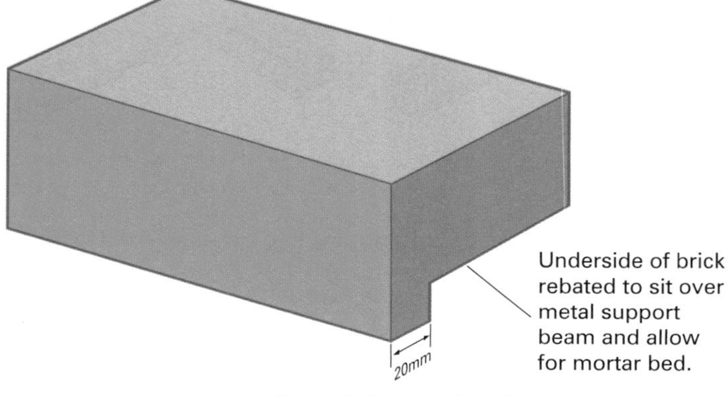

Figure 8.6 A pistol brick

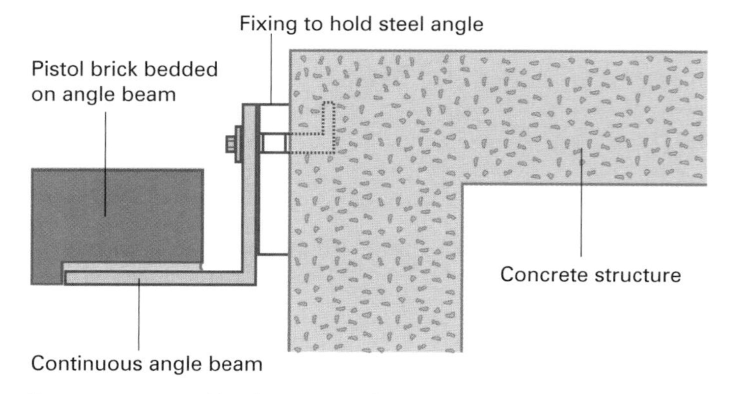

Figure 8.7 A pistol brick positioned on the supporting metal beam

Where this joint is excessive, in other words above the normal 10 mm standard joint, a specially cut brick can be used to reduce the joint thickness. This brick is commonly referred to as a pistol brick. These are normally specially made for individual building projects.

The pistol brick is a standard size brick rebated on its underside to allow it to fit over the edge of the support beam, thus reducing the appearance of the excessive joint.

FAQ

Why do you need to use a pistol brick to reduce the size of the joint between the angle and the course laid on top of it?

A joint which is excessive in size (above the normal 10 mm) will look unsightly and out of place, particularly where the brickwork is a prominent feature.

In instances where cavity widths exceed the normal 75 mm, which is becoming increasingly more common, particularly on cladded structures, the metal angle support is supported by individual metal brackets spaced at smaller distances apart and fixed back to the structure. These individual brackets can be specially made to suit the cavity width. In addition, the thickness of the angle support beam can be reduced slightly due to the frequency in the spacing of the individual brackets, thus giving greater support. This type of bracket is normally supported by fixing into a channel which is pre-cast into the concrete structure or fixed directly to a steel structure.

Where it is necessary to clad elevations which are curved, or where there needs to be an arch or soldier course incorporated above an opening, single bracket supports are required. Continuous metal angles are not manufactured to suit this type of work.

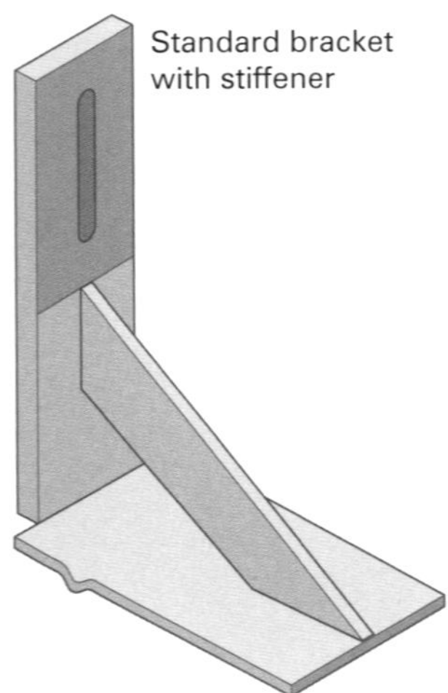

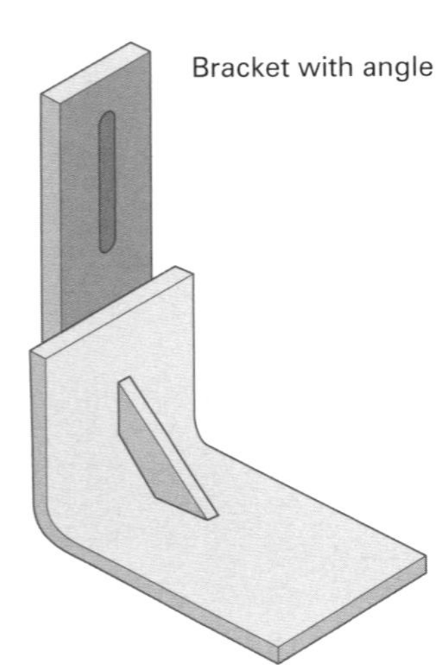

Figure 8.8 Single support brackets

Remember

If you do not ensure the supports are levelled at the time of fixing your brickwork, cladding will not be level and will look unsightly

Maintaining accuracy and stability

Whatever system is being used to support cladding, it is essential to ensure that all support systems are fixed to the main structure securely. Manufacturers' guidelines will identify how tightly fixings are to be secured and how the various components of a particular fixing should be put together.

Additional support for cladding

Up to now we have only referred to the need for supporting and securing cladding at storey height. In addition to this support, it is also essential to provide **lateral** support to the cladding. Lateral support will help to prevent the masonry cladding buckling under the various stresses, caused by **compressive forces**.

Definition

Lateral – belonging to, relating to, located at or affecting the side

Compressive forces – these relate to the weight

Lateral support is provided in two ways when installing masonry cladding. The first method of providing lateral support is to tie the inner leaf to the outer leaf using traditional methods of positioning ties. Obviously the type of tie to be used will be determined by the type of structure.

The second method used to provide lateral support is by tying the cladding to the structure using a lateral restraint tie system. One such method of providing lateral support is a system which comprises of a series of sliding ties fixed to a vertical support rod. This rod is then fixed to the main structural frame. The sliding ties can be positioned at appropriate points on the vertical rod which coincide with bed joints of the brick cladding, as it is constructed.

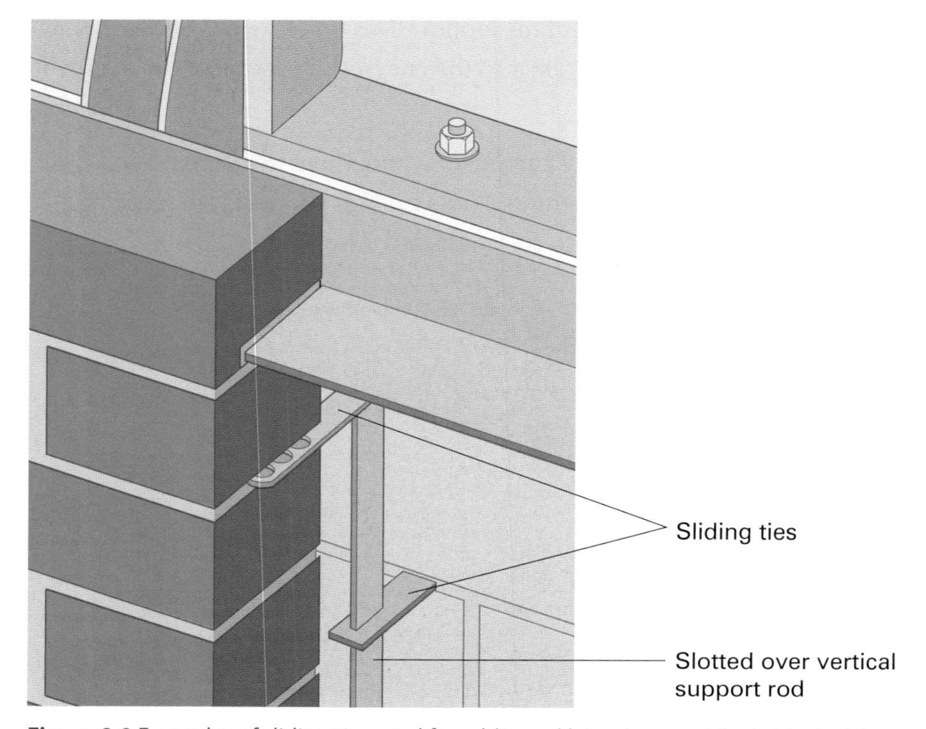

Figure 8.9 Examples of sliding ties used for additional lateral support for brick cladding

Basic principles of construction

Whether building traditional cavity walling or installing masonry cladding which incorporates a cavity type construction, the principles of preventing water or moisture penetrating into the inner leaf of the building are the same.

Cavity trays and weep holes need to be positioned as shown in Figure 8.10.

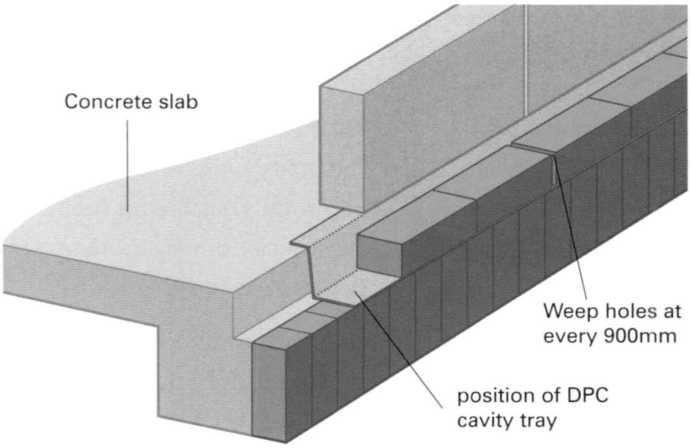

Figure 8.10 The positioning of cavity tray and weep holes

When laying the course of bricks directly onto the metal support angle or concrete support beam, the bricklayer must ensure there is a minimum of two-thirds of the brick's width actually bearing on the angle or beam. As we have previously discussed, pistol bricks may be used on this course to reduce the width of the oversized joint formed by the angle and DPC.

Earlier in this chapter we looked at the provision of horizontal movement joints to compensate for compressive forces imposed on the brick cladding sections. In addition to these movement joints it is also important to take into consideration sideways movement caused by expansion or contraction of the brickwork. This can be compensated for by introducing vertical movement joints. These are introduced where the lengths of the brick cladding sections exceed 9m.

Refer to Chapter 11 in *Brickwork Level 2* which deals with the provision of expansion joints.

Note

Where sections of cladding are separated by vertical movement joints there is still a need to tie the sections together. Special movement joint ties are available for this

Supporting cladding above openings

Cladding above openings can either be of purpose made sections or suspended brickwork, i.e. brick soldier courses.

Cladding panels can be produced by securing brick slips or tiles to a steel lintel section or purpose made load-bearing unit. The disadvantage of using these types of cladding is that the support angle can be seen where the opening is bridged.

In order to alleviate this problem, a brick soldier course can be suspended from the main structure above the opening using specially designed metal support brackets. These brackets are individual and incorporate stirrups which support steel rods threaded through the perforations in the suspended bricks.

There is a need to temporarily support the brickwork during construction to prevent sinking or sagging of the suspended brickwork. This support is normally in the form of a timber frame built to the size of the opening which is removed once the brick mortar has fully **cured**.

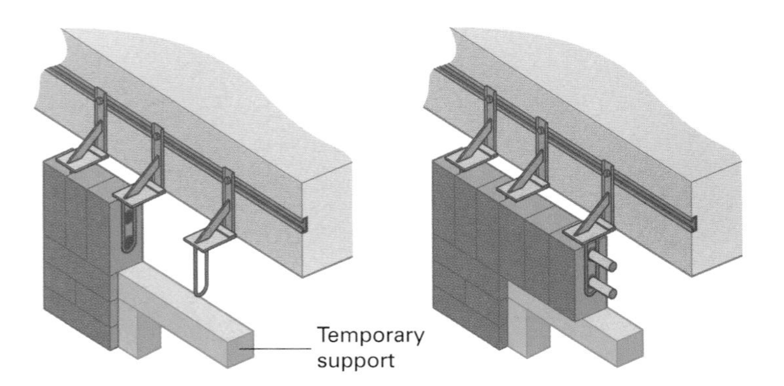

Figure 8.11 The use of stirrup brackets to suspend brickwork above an opening

Definition

Cured – the mortar has set and reached its full strength

Definition

Pre-fabricated - refers to cladding components which are pre-made and designed to minimise the amount of installation work required

Fixing of alternative cladding methods

This section will introduce you to just two of the many types of brick slip or tile systems currently available on today's market. This type of cladding is more commonly known as **pre-fabricated**.

One such method involves the fixing of timber studs to the main framework to which individual brick course units are secured.

As each cladding unit is fixed it must be levelled across its length. Each unit slots into the one below and is then fixed back to the vertical timbers as shown in Figure 8.12. Individual units can be cut to the required lengths using a mechanical brick saw.

Individual units can also be pre-fabricated to provide special brick details such as dentil courses, corbelling courses, soldier courses, arch designs, etc.

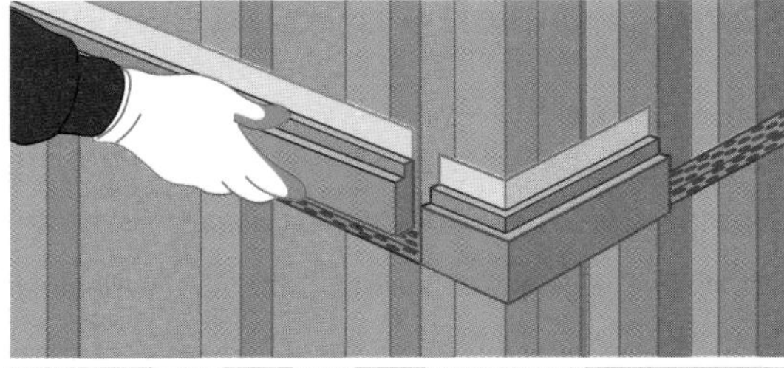

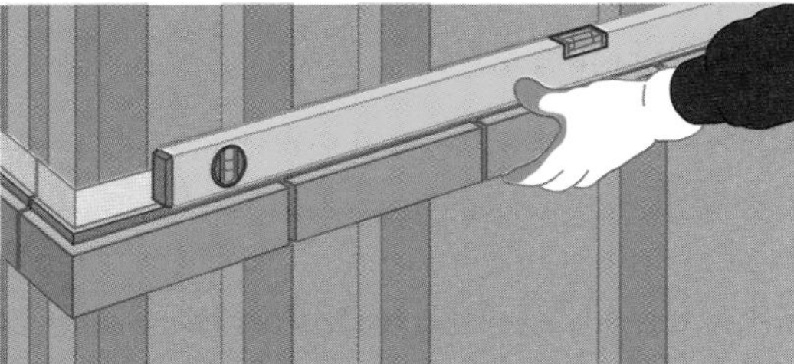

Figure 8.12 Individual brick course cladding with rebate for fixing to timber studs

Where the cladding butts up to a window or door frame, the joint is sealed using an appropriate coloured mastic sealant.

Once the cladding system has been installed, the vertical and horizontal joints between the brick tiles are filled with mortar using a mortar application bag or jointing gun. When the mortar has sufficiently dried it is jointed in the normal way.

Another method of installing pre-fabricated cladding involves fixing a lightweight steel framework to the main structure using a similar principle to that used with the timber studs detailed above. A cement based backing sheet is fixed, mechanically, to the steel frame. Brick slips or tiles are then stuck to the backing sheet using a specially made adhesive.

As with the first system, the joints are filled with mortar and jointed as appropriate.

This type of system can be used on main structures of either concrete or steel.

On the job: Using lateral sliding support ties

A young bricklaying apprentice has been given the task of building the final section of brick cladding on a concrete structure whilst the experienced bricklayers carry out the setting out of an adjoining structure. The apprentice has almost completed the section when he realises that he has forgotten to put in place the lateral sliding support ties fixed to the main structure, although he has put in place the lateral support ties connecting the inner and outer leaves of the cavity walling.

On speaking to another apprentice he is told not to worry as long as he has incorporated the normal cavity ties.

What should he do? Does he need to inform the experienced bricklayers and rebuild the section or does he agree with the other apprentice and complete the work without the sliding ties?

Remember

There are numerous different systems now in use, and we have only touched on a small number, but whatever system you come across, remember the manufacturer's installation instructions must be followed. Not only will this guide you on how to carry out the work it will ensure the cladding does its job and will not fail over time

Knowledge check

1. What is meant when walls are referred to as load-bearing?
2. Pre-cast brick cladding panels are much thicker in section than traditional brick outer leaves – true or false?
3. Name two materials other than clay brick used for cladding.
4. Traditionally support for cladding on concrete structures is provided by the use of toe beams and what other type of beam?
5. What is the name given to the rebated brick used to reduce the size of the joint where brick cladding sits on the metal support beam?
6. What metal support system is used to tie cladding back to a curved structure and why?
7. What is meant by compressive forces?
8. What is the minimum bearing that should be achieved when bedding a brick on a metal support angle?
9. What is the attachment on a metal support bracket called which supports a suspended soldier brick?
10. On pre-fabricated cladding, jointing is carried out as the work proceeds – true or false?

chapter 9

Decorative panels

OVERVIEW

The main purpose of adding decorative features to brick walling is to enhance the appearance and aesthetic value of long, flat lengths of walling. There are many methods and bonding arrangements which can be used to create these decorative features. This chapter deals with one of the methods of providing them - the use of decorative panels. Other methods and bonding arrangements were dealt with in more detail in Chapter 6.

Decorative work must be of the highest quality of craftsmanship in order to achieve the desired effect. Good planning and setting out is essential as there is very little room for error in decorative brickwork. Materials should also be carefully selected as flawed or sub-standard materials will be even more visible, as the feature in which they are used is the main focal point for the untrained eye.

This chapter is intended to familiarise you with the different bonding arrangements and the methods used for constructing decorative panels and will cover the following aspects:

- Types of panels and bonding arrangements
- Preparation and setting out for decorative panels
- Construction methods for decorative panels.

Decorative panels

Types of panels and bonding arrangements

Types of panel

There are three variations to the way in which decorative panels can be presented. These are:

- flush with the face
- recessed
- projecting.

Flush with the face

This is where the decorative panel insert is built flush with the face of the main wall.

Recessed

This is where the decorative panel insert is built back from the face of the main wall.

Projecting

This is where the decorative panel insert is built projecting out past the face of the main walling. The projection is normally no more than 25 mm.

Bonding arrangements

There are three main bonding arrangements for use in decorative panels. However, all three have variations.

The three main bonding arrangements are:

- basket weave
- herringbone
- interlacing.

Note

The recessed panel is only recommended for solid wall construction as the panel insert is usually recessed by approximately 38 mm and this would mean that in a cavity wall construction, the cavity width would be reduced due to the bricks being set back in the panel. This removes the minimum cavity width requirement

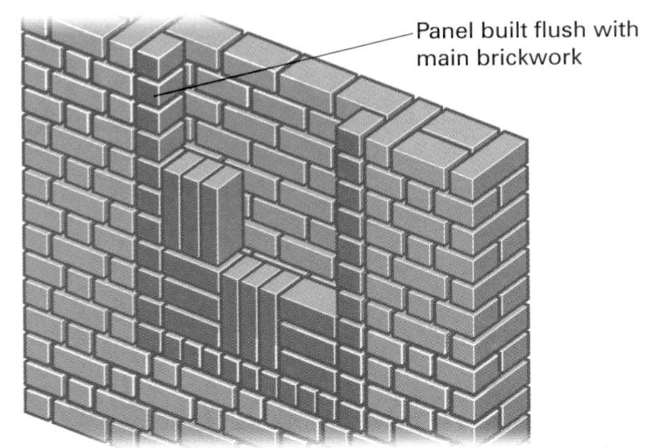

Figure 9.1 A decorative panel insert built flush with the face of the main wall

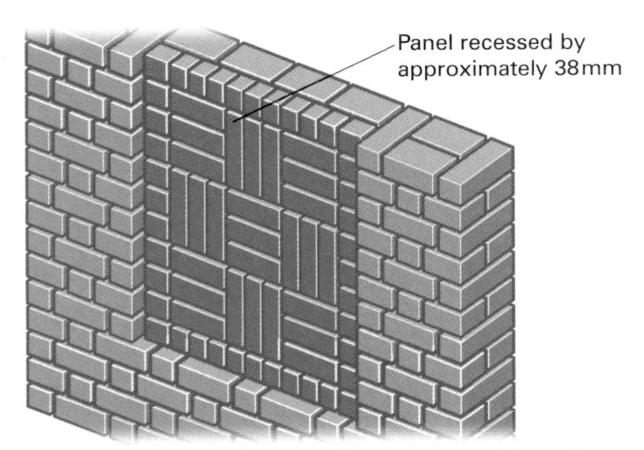

Figure 9.2 A decorative panel insert recessed from the face of the main wall

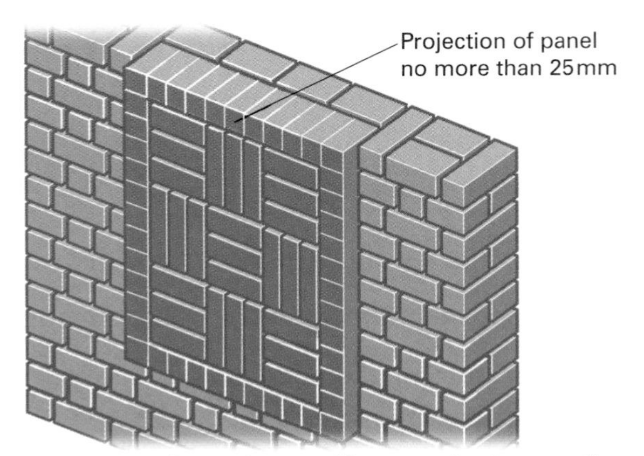

Figure 9.3 A decorative panel insert projecting past the face of the main wall

Basket weave

This is the most straightforward of bonding arrangements as very little setting out is required in comparison to other arrangements used in decorative panels. As you can clearly see from Figure 9.4, basket weave consists of three stretchers laid on top of each other, followed by three soldiers laid next to them and on top of them.

A variation to basket weave bond is diagonal basket weave. This is where the basket weave arrangement described above is laid at a 45° angle to the base of the panel. This arrangement requires setting out and a large amount of cutting.

When setting the panel out dry, prior to cutting and laying the bricks, further variations to this bond can be formed. One such way is to use one of the main continuous joints as a diagonal joint passing through the centre of the panel in both directions, (see Figure 9.6). This will give the impression of a diamond shape in the centre of the panel, which could be further enhanced with the use of coloured mortar around the border of the diamond shape and the bricks within the shape.

Another option is to use the centre of the middle brick of the panel positioned over the point where the 45° diagonal setting out lines cross (see Figure 9.7).

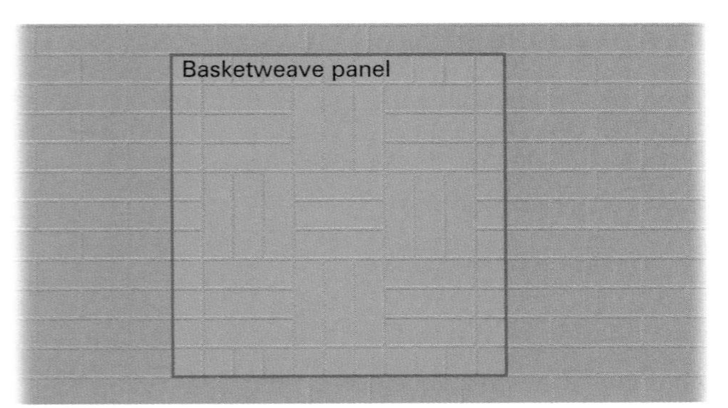

Figure 9.4 A decorative panel insert in basket weave

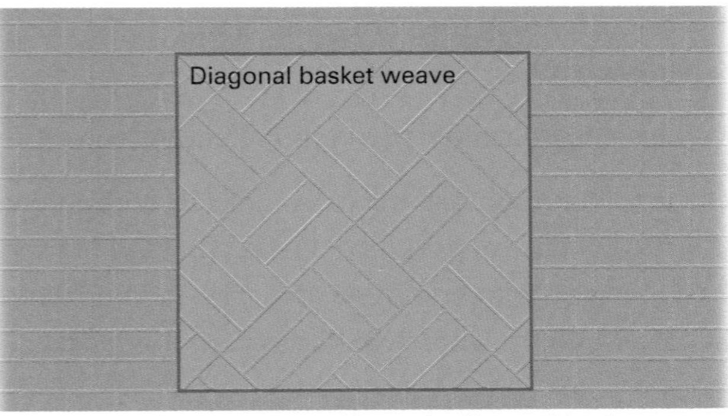

Figure 9.5 A decorative panel insert in diagonal basket weave

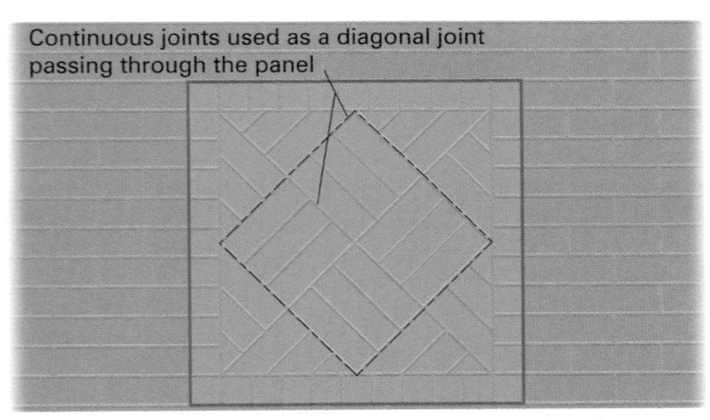

Figure 9.6 Continuous joints positioned centrally within a panel to form a diamond shape

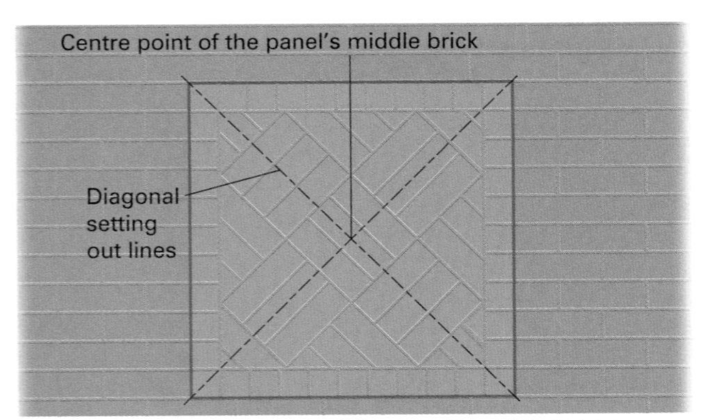

Figure 9.7 The centre point of the panel's middle brick is positioned over the point where the diagonal setting out lines cross

Did you know?

Where three stretchers are laid on top of each other, this arrangement is known as 'stack bond'

Note

As with diagonal basket weave, vertical and horizontal herringbone bonding arrangements require accurate setting out and a significant amount of cutting

Herringbone

There are three main variations to this type of bond and they are:

- vertical herringbone
- horizontal herringbone
- diagonal herringbone.

All of the above herringbone arrangements have one common factor and that is that the bricks forming the pattern are laid at 90° to each other.

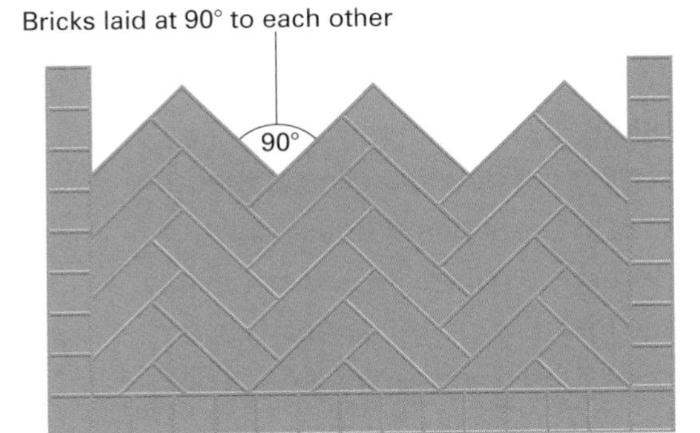

Figure 9.8 Bricks laid at 90° to each other to form herringbone bond

Vertical and horizontal herringbone patterns are also laid at 45° to the base line of the panel.

Diagonal herringbone requires much less cutting than vertical and horizontal and setting out is also minimal. This is due to the fact that the herringbone pattern is laid in a similar way to basket weave with bricks laid vertically and horizontally off the base line of the panel and not at 45° as with the other two herringbone variations.

All of the above herringbone arrangements can be built using double bricks as opposed to the standard singular brick arrangement. It is not surprising to learn that these are referred to as:

- double vertical herringbone
- double horizontal herringbone
- double diagonal herringbone bond.

Remember

Wherever possible, when constructing decorative panels, cuts should be made using a table saw/ cutter or portable power cutter. This makes cutting more accurate and there is less wastage

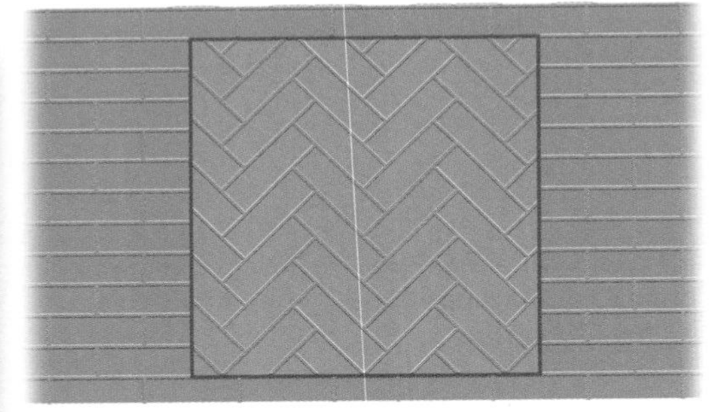

Figure 9.9 Vertical herringbone

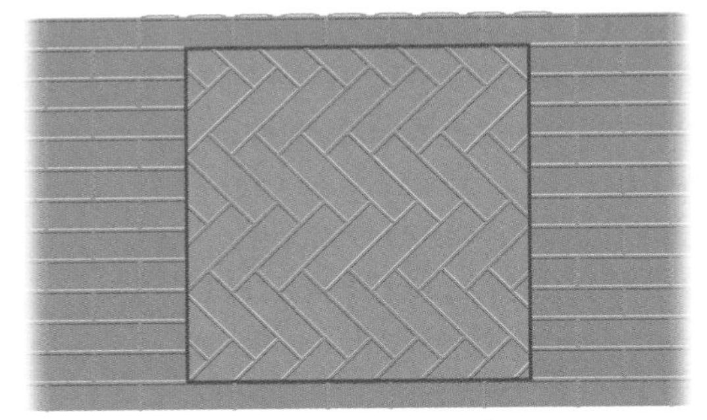

Figure 9.10 Horizontal herringbone

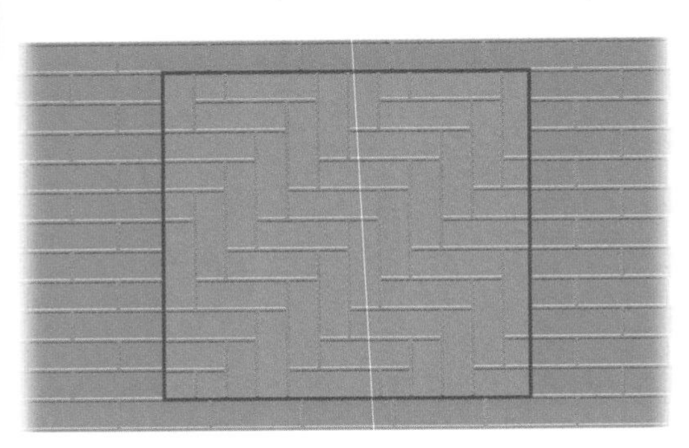

Figure 9.11 Diagonal herringbone

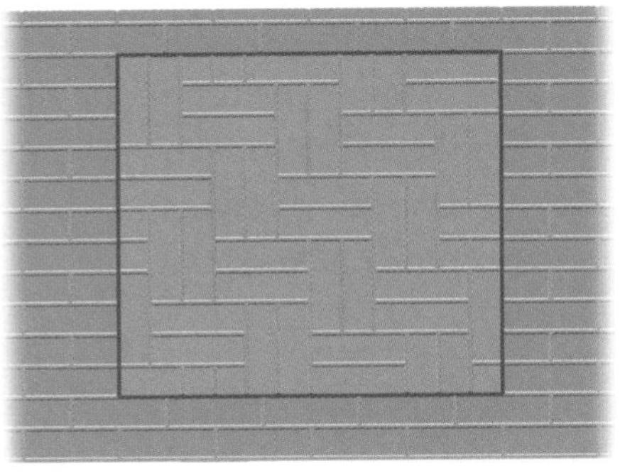

Figure 9.12 Double diagonal herringbone

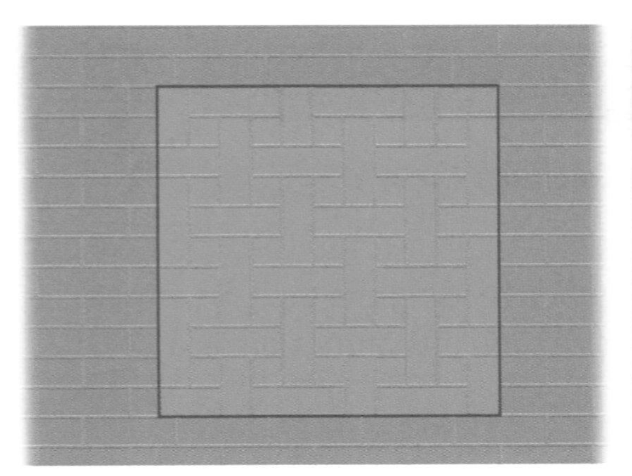

Figure 9.13 Interlacing bond

Figure 9.14 Diagonal interlacing bond

Interlacing bond

As with all of the other bonds mentioned, interlacing bond can also be laid diagonally. The diagonal version of this bond requires more cutting than any of the other bonds.

As you can see from the illustrations above, interlacing bond uses both 1/3 brick cuts and 2/3 brick cuts to achieve the interlacing effect. Diagonal interlacing also has the additional angled cuts around the perimeter of the panel insert.

The interlacing bond is the less commonly used of all decorative panels. This is because of the amount of cuts required which make it time consuming and costly (where the bricks are cut by hand).

Preparation and setting out for decorative panels

Preparation

For all decorative panels, except basket weave and interlacing bond, the opening in which the panel insert is to sit should be built first. As basket weave and interlacing bond patterns coincide with brick courses, this type of panel can be built as the work proceeds.

One method of ensuring that the correct opening size is maintained is by using a **'pinch rod'**.

Find Out

Are there any other variations or types of bonding arrangements used in decorative feature work which have not been covered in this chapter?

Note

When preparing it is of the utmost importance to ensure that the reveals of the opening are kept plumb and to gauge during construction. If accuracy is not maintained the bonding arrangement will not fit the opening size and will look flawed in its appearance, thus defeating the object of producing a pleasing decorative feature

Definition

Pinch rod – a piece of timber cut to the size of the opening and used to measure the distance between the reveals at various stages during their construction

Note

If a concrete floor surface is used in step 1 you must ensure that this is an out of the way, unused area. This will prevent the dry bonded panel being disturbed during the setting out and cutting process

Note

How the bricks are positioned on the starting point depends upon the bonding arrangement being used. (See the earlier section on bonding arrangements on pages 132–5)

Good idea

When drawing the vertical and horizontal centre lines onto the chosen surface, make sure that they extend past the outline of the panel. This ensures that, when the panel outline is covered by the dry bonded bricks, the centre lines can still be determined to aid the remainder of the setting out process

FAQ

Why not use a steel tape measure to check the width at varying points?

There is always a risk of human error when reading the tape measure; a piece of timber cut at the accurate size required cannot be read incorrectly.

Setting out

As previously stated, basket weave, diagonal herringbone and double diagonal herringbone are the only bonding arrangements which require little or no setting out prior to laying. However, care must still be taken during construction to ensure that each brick within the panel is laid plumb and to the correct angle.

The setting out process for diagonal basket weave and herringbone bonding arrangements are much the same.

Step 1

Draw the outline of the panel opening on a suitable surface. This surface can be either a flat concrete floor or a piece of sturdy sheet material such as plywood.

At the time of drawing the panel on the flat surface you need to remember to draw the outline 20 mm shorter in its width than the actual opening size. This allows for a 10 mm mortar joint on each side, between the reveal and the panel insert bricks. You also need to deduct 10 mm from the actual height of the opening size to allow for the bed joint.

Step 2

With the outline of the panel now drawn you need to mark out centre lines both vertically and horizontally onto the surface (see Figure 9.15).

From these centre lines you must now mark diagonal centre lines at 45° (see Figure 9.16). This provides the starting point for the centre bricks of the panel.

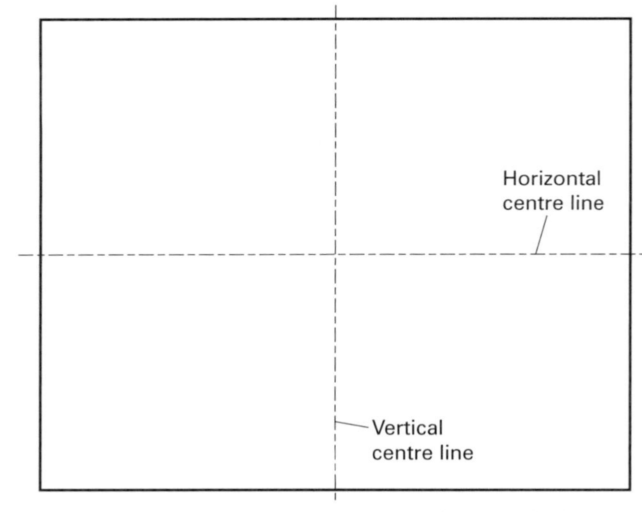

Figure 9.15 Vertical and horizontal centre lines marked on a panel outline

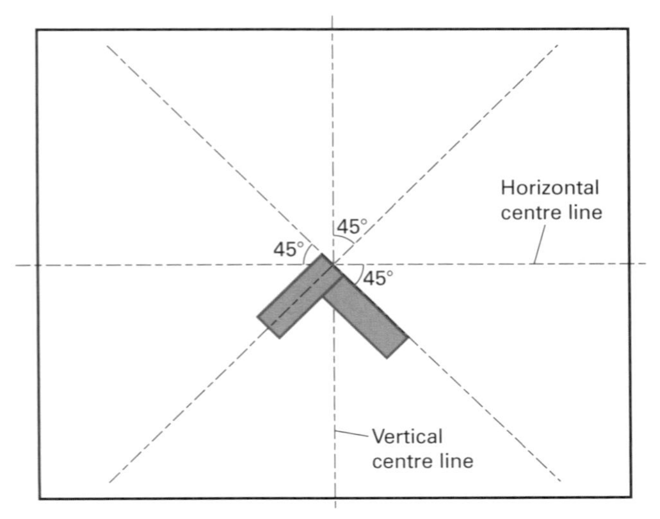

Figure 9.16 Diagonal centre lines drawn at 45° to the vertical and horizontal centre lines

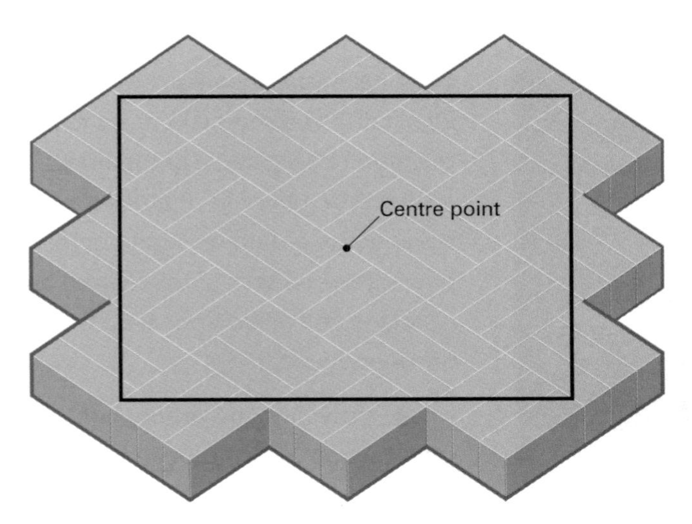

Figure 9.17 The panel size drawn on top of the dry bonded bricks

Step 3

Once the position of the central bricks has been determined, you need to position the remainder of the bricks required to complete the panel. At this point you must ensure that they are laid accurately at the correct angle and with the correct joint thickness between all bricks.

Step 4

Using the extended vertical and horizontal centre lines as a guide, you must now mark out the panel size, drawn on the flat surface, on top of the dry bonded bricks (see Figure 9.17).

Step 5

You now need to carry out all the required cutting.

Note

In step 3 you are looking to produce the finished effect in terms of appearance.
It is only now, prior to cutting, that any flaws or inaccuracies can be put right

Construction methods

Ensuring accuracy when laying the first course of cuts at the bottom of the panel is essential in order to maintain the correct angle and gauge.

It is advisable to fix a temporary piece of timber across the face of the main wall, level with the top of the course from which the panel insert will be started.

This temporary piece of timber can be used to mark out the position of each of the cuts, including mortar joints, along the bottom of the panel.

When constructing flush or projecting panel inserts, it is also important to use a line and pins to maintain the face plane of the feature. When building a recessed panel, it is difficult to use a line and pins so a straight edge which has been cut to fit inside the panel recess can be used (see Figure 9.18).

Safety tip

If you are using a table type brick cutter or powered brick cutter of any kind you must have been fully trained and deemed competent to use it. Do not change any abrasive cutting wheel unless you have an abrasive wheels certificate. Be safe not sorry!

Note

A line and pins should also be used to maintain the level across the top of each course within the panel, particularly when constructing basket weave, diagonal or double diagonal herringbone. This is because the frequency of continuity within the horizontal bed joints is greater and more pronounced

Definition

Vial – a small glass bottle containing the bubble used to give a reading when plumbing or levelling brick or block work

When laying other herringbone patterns or diagonal basket weave, a boat level with an adjustable **vial** should be used to maintain the required 45° angle of the bricks. It is advisable to check each and every brick is laid at the required 45° angle. This will prevent the pattern of the feature becoming distorted and avoid unnecessary taking down and rebuilding.

Finally, providing the setting out and construction work has been carried out correctly, the cuts at the top of the panel should sit in line with the top of the reveals and there should be no need for further cutting.

All of the bonding arrangements covered within this chapter can be further enhanced in their appearance by introducing a border around the panel insert. This border is normally made up of bricks laid header wise and allowed to project or sit back from the main face wall, in line with the panel insert (see Figure 9.19). The use of coloured mortar in this border will further highlight the feature.

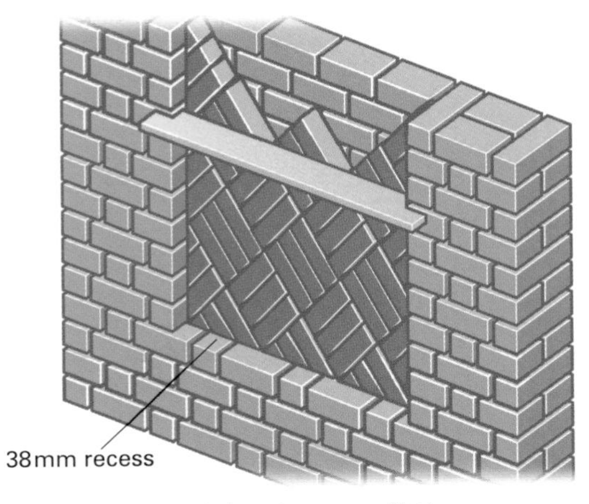

Figure 9.18 A straight edge cut to fit the panel recess

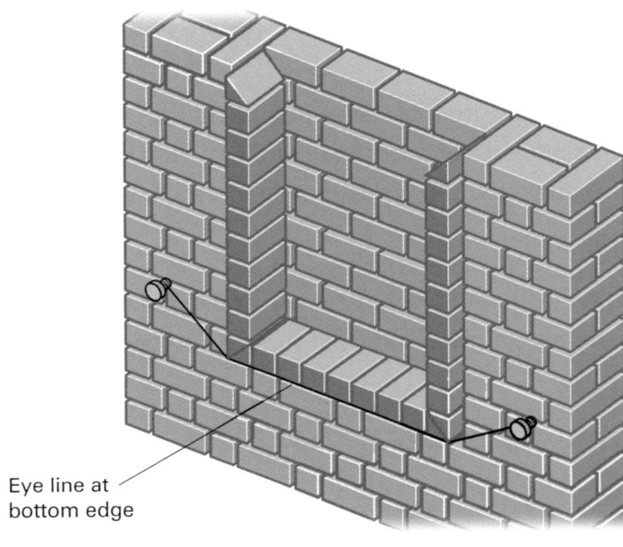

Figure 9.19 A panel insert with a border

On the job: Vijay's problem panel

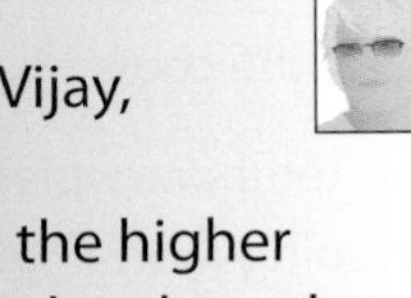

Whilst constructing a decorative panel in vertical herringbone, Vijay, a young apprentice, has noticed that the vertical joint between the reveals and the cuts of the panel insert has begun to widen the higher the work gets. It has been suggested by another apprentice that he alters the remaining cuts to compensate for the wider joint.

What is the possible cause of this and how should it be put right?

Knowledge check

1. What is the purpose of decorative features?
2. Why should materials be carefully selected for use in decorative work?
3. Name the three main bonding arrangements used in decorative panels.
4. What is the variation to basket weave?
5. When setting out any bonding arrangement, on what can the outline of the panel be marked?
6. How much should be deducted from the width of the panel size when marking out for a decorative panel insert?
7. Why should the vertical and horizontal centre lines be extended past the outline of the panel when setting out?
8. At what angle are the diagonal centre lines set out for herringbone bond?
9. Describe basket weave bond.
10. Why is interlacing bond considered costly and time consuming?

chapter 10

Repairing and maintaining masonry structures

OVERVIEW

Some home owners are reluctant to move house and decide to carry out alterations to their home to improve it, either by adding extra space or by changing the current layout of the property. The latter can include taking out walls or putting openings into existing walls to create more space in certain rooms. Home owners may also want to carry out simple repairs or maintenance of the decorative appearance or general upkeep of the property.

This chapter will explain the basic ways repairs and maintenance can be achieved and will cover the following:

- Adding space to a property
- Changing the existing layout
- Repairs and maintenance
- Material delivery

Definition

Outbuilding – a shed or storage area connected to the main building

Adding space to a property

There are several ways in which a property can have space added. These could include:

- building an extension to give extra space or an extra room or rooms
- adding a conservatory
- converting roof space (the loft)
- changing the use of a garage or **outbuilding**.

Extensions

This is where extra space is gained by adding an extra room or rooms to the current structure, whether it is single storey or double storey. If an extension is to be built, planning permission or building regulation approval must be gained from the local council prior to the start of any work.

Foundations must be dug to meet local authority approval, as with any new building with a cavity wall construction.

The external appearance must match that of the existing property, so you must make sure that the brick you use is as close a match as possible. The brick type may be stated in the specification or it may state 'to match existing'. If you are unsure of the type of brick, take a sample to a builders' merchant and ask them if they can either match the brick or tell you what type it is. If it is an older property, the company that made the original bricks may no longer be in production as many of the small independent companies have closed or been swallowed up by the large conglomerates. Some merchants have their own brick libraries showing most of the bricks that are manufactured today which is a great help when choosing the right bricks. You also need to match to the same brick sizes as older properties would have used imperial bricks which are different to the metric sizes produced today.

Remember

The brick needs to be matched before the work is priced as it could prove very costly if you have not allowed enough money. The local authority could reject the bricks if they are not correct

In addition, all windows must match the existing profiles and materials used (wood or UPVC being the most commonly found although some properties may have wood frames with aluminium infills). These would generally be stated in the specification for the work or on the drawings supplied.

The extension must be joined correctly to the main structure with the cavity continuous throughout; this process is usually started just below DPC level as the damp course also requires lapping to the existing to prevent moisture rising up at the joining point. The mortar joint at DPC level must be cut out with a brick saw or disc cutter to allow the DPC to be slid into position and the join re-pointed.

Prior to the joining of the DPC, the cavity must be extended. This is done by marking the existing wall at the back of the face brick line and plumbing and marking this line vertically to the height required for joining. From this line the cavity width size is marked and the same process carried out. These two lines are then carefully cut using a disc cutter, ensuring that the material is cut right through to the cavity to ensure less vibration of material at the next stage. The material is then cut out to leave an open cavity which is the size required for the extension.

Now the cavity has been cut, the new external brickwork has to be joined as well as the internal block work. This process is carried out by **toothing** the external face brickwork and internal block work.

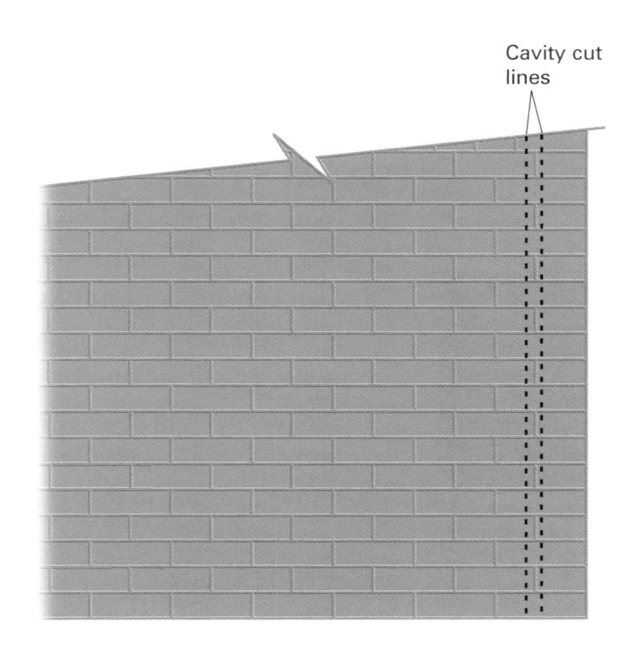

Figure 10.1 The marking of cavity position

Joining the face brickwork

The face brickwork is joined to the existing wall by means of toothing - cutting out brickwork on each course to accommodate the new external wall. The amount to be cut out is determined by the type of bond used on the existing brickwork and the position of the extended wall. If the new wall is built to an existing corner on a stretcher bonded wall (half bond), the half bat remaining from the original cavity cutting is removed, allowing for new brickwork. If the existing wall is built in Flemish or English bond (quarter bond), then the half bat and closer is removed. The toothing will determine the bonding of each course. Therefore this must be decided at an early stage to ensure that brickwork showing above ground level works to the toothed brickwork for bond or, if this is not possible, suitable cuts are used within the new wall.

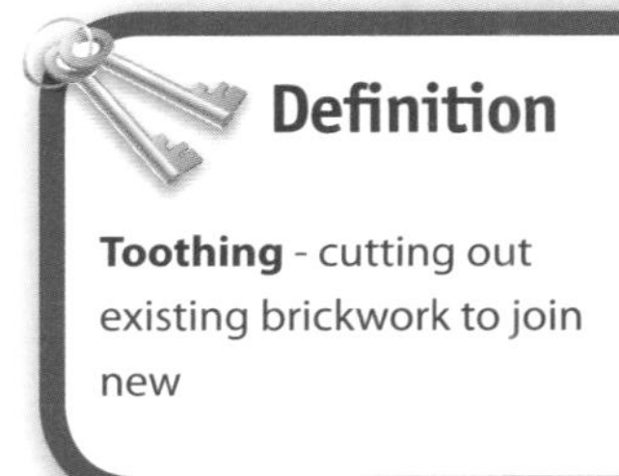

Toothing - cutting out existing brickwork to join new

If the toothing is to be elsewhere along the wall then only the width of the brick plus a joint thickness needs to be cut on alternate courses (but you will still need to think about which course to cut out).

¼ toothing in english bond

Half bond toothing

Figure 10.2 Toothing for half and quarter bond

Cutting the brick toothing

You must take great care not to damage the remaining brickwork around the area when cutting out the brick toothing ready for the new wall. Several methods can be used for cutting but certain factors will determine the best one. If the brickwork is older, with a sand and lime mix, the joints may be fairly soft. Therefore it may be possible to cut the bed joint with a masonry saw and to tap the brick out carefully. If the joint is made of sand and cement, then a small disc cutter will be required. The cutting must be carried out very carefully so that the surrounding bricks are not damaged – you would need to remove any remaining brickwork if the blade touches it. Chipping bricks is also a hazard whilst carrying out this task. In some instances a hammer and sharp chisel may be used but, again, great care must be taken not to chip or crack and break the surrounding brickwork. The bricks should be cut by gradually cutting one small section at a time, angling the chisel to cut the middle and back areas first and then the front area so that you don't put too much pressure on the surrounding brickwork.

Note

With all toothing, always start from the top and work downwards

The block work

The cutting process to accommodate the block work is almost the same as for brickwork except that three bricks are cut out each time and the width may vary to suit different thicknesses of blocks. This is aptly called block toothing or block bonding. The toothing must work out to accommodate the block courses so that they line up with the brickwork.

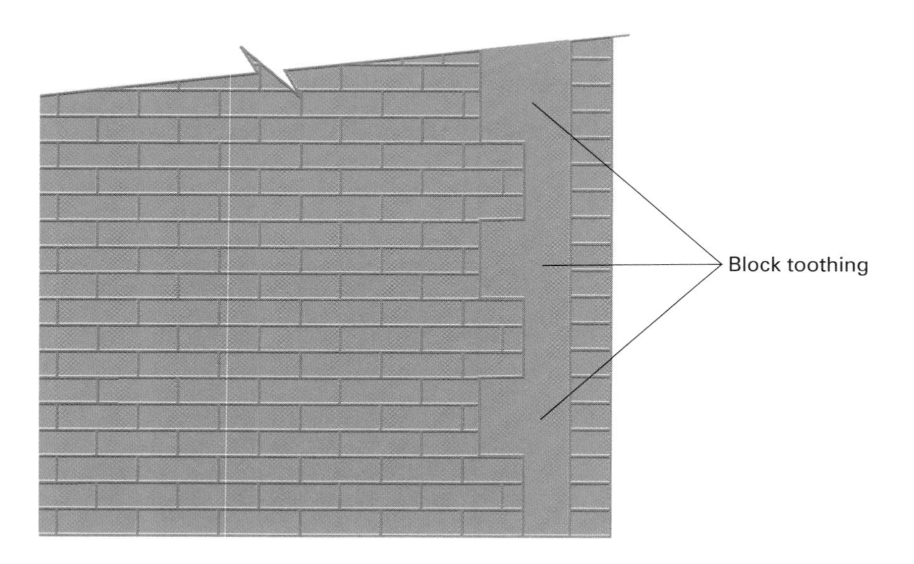

Figure 10.3 Block toothing

Alternative joining

In some instances, proprietary wall connectors may be used rather than cutting out the brickwork toothing. There are several different types available from builders' merchants and they can be made of galvanised steel or stainless steel. If used on external walls, only the stainless steel type should be used. They are fixed to the wall by means of coach bolts and wall plugs. Therefore the wall requires drilling, normally with a 10 mm masonry drill.

This system is used because it is quicker to fix than toothing and causes less vibration or damage to the existing brickwork. The cost of buying the connectors then outweighs the time and effort required for toothing. However, permission must be granted before use so look on the drawings to see if they are specified or ask the local authority if they can be used.

Standard of work

The standard of work should match the existing work so that the joint finish should match as well as the colour of the mortar joint. This could be achieved by producing several different mix proportions in small quantities, leaving them to dry and then choosing the most suitable.

Changing the existing layout

Forming openings

Altering the inside of a property can give more space to areas which are used more than others. For example, older properties may have a separate lounge and dining area and this can be changed to make one larger room by taking out the adjoining wall or by forming an opening to allow access from one room to the other. This could also be the case for separate toilet and bathroom areas or kitchen/diners or even enlarging bedrooms. The layout is designed to suit the customer but the changes are based on the same construction principles - taking out existing brick or block work but at the same time ensuring that the structural stability is not affected.

Find out

Find out how loads are calculated and what type of lintels you should use for a specific job

The same principles apply with all openings: the weight above the opening must be supported by a lintel and the bearing of the lintel must be sufficient to take the weight that has been transferred.

To form any new opening in existing brickwork, the wall above needs to be supported. Checks need to be made to ascertain the extent of the weight to be transferred. The main areas to look at include:

- Does the wall continue above on the next floor or, if it is an upstairs room, into the roof space?
- Do the ceiling joists above sit onto the wall, transferring the weight of the room's furniture onto the wall?

How do we check for this?

Visual inspection will show if the wall above is load bearing. In the case of a standard size door opening, there will be brickwork in the existing room that will require supporting as well as anything above. If it is impossible to tell then the original drawings with measurements will provide this information.

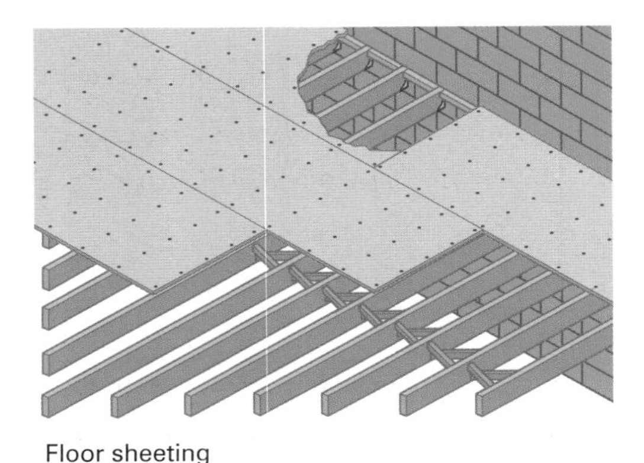

Figure 10.4 Floorings and fixings

A visual check of the upstairs floorboards will tell you which way the ceiling joists run, as the joists will run the opposite way. If the flooring has been replaced with chipboard sheeting, then the lines of nailing will show the joists. This means that any carpets in the room must be rolled back sufficiently to make the checks.

These checks give us a lot of information about how the weight needs to be temporarily supported whilst the brickwork is removed and the lintel is inserted.

The temporary support system is called dead shoring and is used to carry vertical loads. The system is comprised of props that support timber or steel which is positioned either on both sides of the wall, or through the wall, depending on the way the joists run. The props used to be made of timber but nowadays they are adjustable steel props called acrows. The acrows are adjustable by means of holes and pins similar to trestles and they have a lever screw system to fine adjust for tightening. They also come in different sizes and can be hired from most plant hire companies.

Note

Be wary if the flooring has been covered with hardboard as this will be fixed down onto the existing flooring but the fixings could be randomly set giving no indication of the positions of the joists. In this instance, an area of the hardboard will need to be removed to confirm the correct joist positions

Positioning of props

Before any work is carried out, all furniture etc. must be moved from the areas so that they are not damaged by the work in progress. Carpets must also be removed or rolled back away from the area and covered. You don't want to incur costly repairs to furniture or carpets which can equal no profit or worse!

When you have found out which way the joists run (see above), you will know how the propping needs to be positioned. There are two different ways to carry out the system based on the way the joists run.

1. parallel to the wall
2. through the wall.

Acrow props

Parallel to the wall

If the joists run directly into the wall to be worked on, two sets of props will be required, one set each side of the wall. The object of this is to transfer the weight temporarily to carry out the work. The props are placed parallel to the new opening area and need to be set back to allow sufficient space to work – this is to ensure that staff don't get injured whilst removing the brickwork and to give sufficient room for working platforms (trestles and boards). Platforms are needed to give enough height to install the lintel when required.

The props should be placed on a scaffold board which must be laid directly onto the floorboards or screed. The scaffold board should be long enough to run past each side of the new opening by at least 1 m. In the case of a standard size door, opening two props each side should be sufficient to carry the weight - they should be positioned no more than 1.5 m apart. A second scaffold board of equal length is to be positioned directly above the floorboard, against the ceiling, with the two props acting as wedges tight between the two boards.

To carry out this operation safely three people will be needed, two to hold and adjust the props and one to hold the board to the ceiling.

The sequence runs as follows:

1. Place the board onto the floorboard or screed, parallel to the wall.
2. Set up the props with the pins roughly in the correct position for the height required.
3. Place the props on the base board and hold in position.
4. Place the second board on top of the two props and temporarily hold from the underside, so as not to trap fingers.
5. Tighten up the props by means of the lever until the board is just about tight to the ceiling.
6. Plumb the props to ensure they are fully upright both ways.
7. Tighten slightly to take up any slack but do not over tighten as you will lift and crack the ceiling line area.
8. Fix nails through the holes in the prop top and base to stop movement.
9. Repeat the sequence to the other side of wall.

Remember

Do not lay base board on to carpets as this will cause damage and allow movement on the props

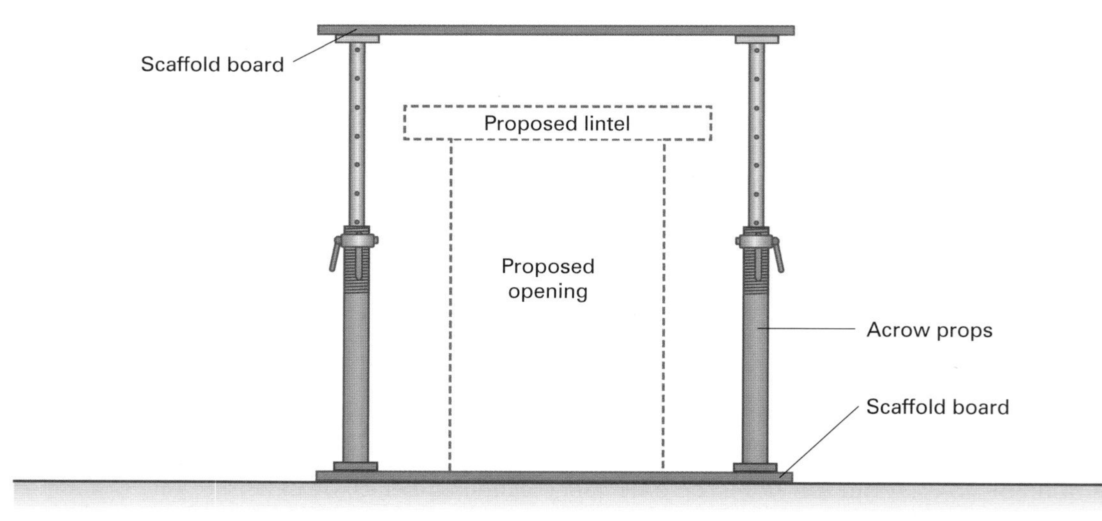

Figure 10.5 Props in position

Through the wall

If the joists run parallel to the wall, no weight from the room is being transferred to the wall. The weight that needs to be supported is only above the immediate area so the props are set to carry this weight. Only two props will be needed to carry out this operation and, instead of a ceiling board, a piece of stout timber (150 mm x 100 mm) or small steel (RSJ) about 2 m long will be needed. This is called a 'needle'.

The sequence for the propping is as follows:

1. Mark out the position of the proposed opening on the wall.
2. Mark the lintel position (for this size of opening a standard 100 mm x 65 mm x 1200 mm is adequate) ensuring equal bearings on both ends.
3. Above the lintel line, mark for a hole at the centre of the opening – it must be large enough for the RSJ or timber to go through.
4. Carefully cut the hole through the wall.
5. The needle is then pushed through the hole leaving equal distance on both sides.
6. A base board needs to be set on the floor on both sides of the wall. If the floor is wooden make sure the base board runs across the joists to transfer any weight.
7. Set up the two props, one on each side of the wall, and adjust the height of the prop to suit the height that the needle comes through the wall.
8. Gently tighten the props until they meet the needle, ensuring that the needle is in a level position. Re-check and adjust the props until the needle is correct.
9. Plumb the props both ways.
10. Finally, tighten both props together so they are firmly in place.
11. Place nails into the prop top and base to stop any movement.

Note

If an RSJ is used as a needle, a timber block needs to be placed between the RSJ and prop to stop any sliding (metal against metal) and for securing the prop

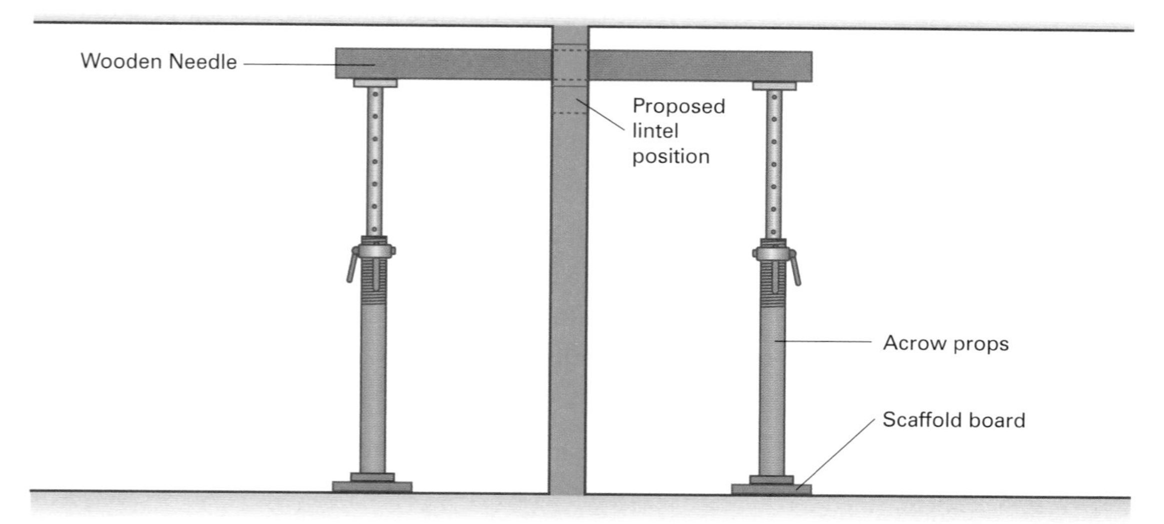

Figure 10.6 Props and needle through wall

Cutting out the opening

Now that the propping is done, you are ready to start the cutting out. The method of cutting is determined by the circumstances of the property. If the property is empty it may be possible to use a disc cutter (but tape the doors to stop the dust travelling right through the property). Care must be taken when you are doing this as the dust produced (and fumes if you are using a petrol cutter) replace the oxygen within that area, so the correct personal protective equipment must be used with frequent breaks taken outside. This is the quickest method but not always the cheapest as the dust will linger for a very long time. If this method is not appropriate then the wall needs to be cut with a hammer and bolster. Another way could be to drill lots of holes along the marking out prior to cutting, but this can be time consuming.

The main thing you must take into account is that, whilst cutting the opening, damage to the surrounding wall must be kept to a minimum so you must be very careful. The type of material the wall is made of may work to your advantage - if it is an older property the internal walls are likely to be made of brick but may have sand/lime joints which will be fairly soft. Newer properties may have lightweight blocks meaning that they will be easier to cut.

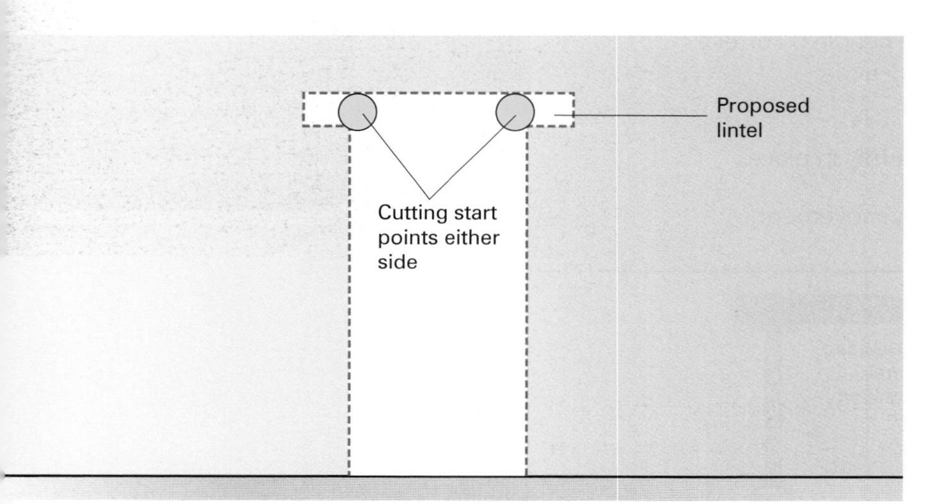

Figure 10.7 The start point for cutting

Cutting by hand tools

Carefully take off the skirting board on both sides of the wall and store it for future reinstatement. Always start the cutting from the top - cut away the plasterwork to the marked lines to the whole of the new lintel area. This will expose the material that the wall is made of. Carefully cut a hole using the nearest joint at the top left or right hand corner near to the plumb line. (Do not cut out the lintel bearing at this stage.)

If the mortar joint is soft, it may be possible to cut the bed joint right across the top of the proposed lintel first and then cut the brick course out from the bed joint below. If not, the course must be cut out in small sections of brickwork so as not to crack or damage the whole wall. In both cases, cut out full bricks only.

Once you have reached the sides, cut the plumb line vertically with a hammer and bolster. If two people are available this can be cut simultaneously from both sides reducing vibration and excess damage.

The whole bricks can be cut out course by course. A saw could be used to cut out a soft perp joint each time to make things easier, and the plumb line cut the same as stated until reaching floor level. The brickwork will need to be cut to below the floor level to allow for finishing at a later date.

At this point, carefully cut out the bearings, making sure no damage is done to the course below as this will eventually take the weight from the lintel area.

If the wall is made of insulation blocks, once a hole has been cut it could be cut with a masonry saw down the plumb lines, as well as horizontally, for the lintel and bearings.

The lintel is then bedded into position. At this point don't bed joint the top of the lintel - allow it to set. Once the bed has set, the top joint should be wedged to the existing brickwork with slate all the way along and then pointed. (If the joint is filled at the time of bedding there is a chance of shrinkage of the joint, causing later movement.)

The opening is now ready for finishing.

Finishing the opening

Any opening can be finished in two different ways:

- by plastering all the exposed edges
- by fitting a lining around the edges.

The lining is normally made of timber.

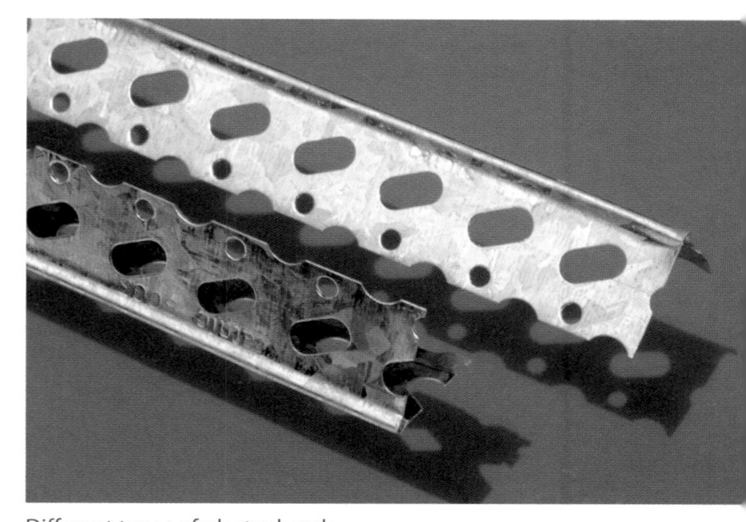

Different types of plaster beads

Plaster finish

If plaster is to be used on all edges as a finish, all the corners must be fitted with a metal angle bead to give a smooth edge to finish the plaster to. There are several different types of beads used in plastering. The main ones are:

- plaster beads
- plasterboard beads
- stop beads.

They all have different uses but produce the same finish, creating an edge to plaster to. Plaster should always be stored in a dry place and used in date order so that it does not harden in the bags before being used.

With the job described here, we will need to use plaster angle beads. These have a galvanised metal edge connected to galvanised wire mesh and are approximately 50 mm wide on each angle. They are fixed into position on the wall by plaster dabs which set quickly to secure in place. To fix them there must be sufficient brickwork exposed and, as the opening plaster was cut flush, you may need to cut the plaster back about 50 mm to take the angle bead. The corner edge of the bead must be set in line with the existing plaster finish and plumbed on the opening internal edge, allowing for at least 15 mm cover of plaster to the wall. This sequence is carried out to all the edges including the underside of the lintel.

Remember

Ensure that the beads are parallel on both sides of the wall

Once all the beads are dry and secured, the plaster can be applied. This is normally in two coats, the first approximately 12 mm thick (but this could depend on the thickness of the existing plaster - it may need to be slightly thicker).

The plaster needs to be applied in thin coats and built up to the required thickness. If sand and cement, or bonding, plaster is used for the first coat, it must be levelled and plumbed using a straight edge or rule. Before the material has set, it should be rubbed over with a wooden float, with nails protruding, to form a key for the finishing plaster. Once dry, the finish plaster is applied and smoothed with a steel plastering trowel. As the plaster dries the surface is slightly dampened with water and re-trowelled to give the finish. The correct timing for this is important to give a smooth sheen to the plaster.

Nowadays, multi-finish plaster is used in most cases. This means that the thickness can be achieved in one coat, gradually building up the thickness as coats are applied and finishing in the same way as previously described.

The floor area where we cut out the bricks now requires finishing with a grit/cement mix of about 1:4 ratio. It must be a minimum of 75 mm thick so that it does not crack and it must be finished smooth to both room levels. DPC may be required below the screed to prevent damp rising. If the finished floor is timber, the boards must be extended between the last joist in each room. You must make sure that the wall below this area does not touch any of the timber as this could cause damp and rot the wood.

When the plaster is dry and the floor is completed, the skirting board can be re-fixed and mitre jointed to the corners on both sides of the wall and through the opening.

Once the plaster is completely dry, i.e. the plaster colour has changed to a very light colour all over, the wall is ready to be painted. A mist coat should be used first as the plaster will draw the paint in, then a minimum of two further coats should be applied.

Lining finish

Rather than having a full plaster finish to the opening, a timber lining can be fitted in the same way as a standard door lining (the difference is that no door stops are fitted). The lining is fitted by the carpenter and the plaster finished as previously described. Once dry the architrave can be fitted.

Larger openings

In the case of larger openings through walls, or complete wall removal, the weight distribution works on the same principles. However, more props need to be used and longer lintels are required. If a whole wall is to be removed, an RSJ will be needed or very substantially-sized timber, normally oak. This may need to be situated on brick piers to take the weight. In cases like this, you may need a structural engineer to determine the size of steel or timber, and the size of piers if required, plus bearings needed. If a full wall is being removed, the steel or timber is normally situated tight to the ceiling line to give maximum headroom to this area. Once situated, the steel is boxed in and can either be plastered or timber lined to create a timber effect.

Repairs and maintenance

All properties need repairs as they get older. The life span of some materials runs out and they have to be repaired or replaced. Some areas that involve the bricklayer are:

- pointing
- cracked bricks or blocks (caused by movement)
- damp problems
- lintel problems.

If we break these down we can investigate the causes and the solutions to correct these problems.

Pointing

The mortar used to build older properties was made up of sand and lime. This is a very soft mortar and, due to weathering or attack, the mortar breaks down. This can happen in small areas or cover whole walls but it needs to be rectified. In *Brickwork Level 2* we explained how to re-point in these situations.

Cracked or broken bricks

Cracked or broken bricks look unsightly in a wall but what needs to be looked at is the reason why it has happened. If a large area has been affected it could be due to movement of the building through subsidence, or it may only be a single brick that was cracked when first laid or had a slight flaw which was not noticed originally.

In the case of large areas, investigation needs to be carried out, especially if there is sizeable cracking and gaps in the bricks and mortar joints. Cracks may have small glass plates screwed across them which are then monitored over a set period to see if movement is still happening. These plates are called 'telltales' and they do what they say; some have a measuring gauge to show movement and others may be plain but if movement occurs they will crack.

Structural engineers are generally involved when a large area is affected, so if you are asked to look at a problem like this it is advisable to inform the client of this straightaway. This problem is probably due to movement in the ground causing the concrete foundation to shift, normally through a crack or sheer. The main reason for movement could be due to:

- shrinkage of the ground structure
- tree roots
- leaking or broken pipes.

Safety tip

If the work is above reachable height, remember to use either a trestle scaffold or tower for the duration of the work - safety is paramount. It may be quicker to use a ladder but not if you fall!

However, there are other factors that could cause movement such as:

- underground railways
- mining
- ground erosion
- long-term bomb damage.

An expert will find the cause and suggest the best way to repair, normally through underpinning the foundation and rebuilding the wall or walls. Underpinning is carried out by specialised companies to specifications set by a structural engineer, or jointly with an architect.

When just single bricks are the cause of the problem, the remedy is to take them out and replace them. Great care is needed when cutting, as well as when matching the brick and mortar colour and finish. Cut small quantities at a time. Chip away at the brick - don't smash at it - the idea is to take out one brick not 20!

Damp problems

Damp penetration can be a major problem, causing staining to interior finishes, bubbling of paintwork to walls and even plaster which is powdering and **blown** on walls.

Definition

Blown - plaster or render no longer adhering to the interior brick or block wall

Other areas that can be affected by damp include timber such as floorboards, joists, skirting boards, window frames, facia and soffit boards which can all rot.

Internal damp is caused in two different ways:

- moisture travelling horizontally
- moisture travelling vertically.

Horizontal moisture

This is normally caused when the cavity is bridged, allowing moisture from the external wall to cross through the cavity into the internal wall. The bridging is usually due to pieces of brick or block dropped down the cavity, either during the original construction or through work carried out at a later time. Mortar bridging the cavity can cause the same problem; this could be caused as explained above or through the breakdown of the material over the course of time, filling the cavity above the DPC and allowing moisture to penetrate across.

How to rectify the problem depends on the area that is affected. If the damp is part way up the wall and affecting a small area, then it could be just a single piece of brick/mortar causing the problem. In some cases, small pieces of timber have been found to be the cause. These will have to be removed by cutting out a brick or two (as previously explained) on the outside wall to investigate – this usually shows the cause. The bridge must then be removed and the bricks replaced.

If the damp is at floor level or just above, the problem could be horizontal or vertical. The cavity could be bridged (as described above) or filled with mortar above the DPC. To rectify this, bricks have to be cut out just above DPC level to see if the cavity is full. If this is the case, then the cavity needs to be fully cleaned to a minimum of 150 mm below DPC level. This may have to be carried out along the whole length of the wall if the findings are bad.

Cleaning out must be done carefully. In some cases the mortar may be very soft and easy to remove but in others it could be firm and very hard to remove. As the cavity is probably 50 mm wide there is not much room to carry this out. Sometimes tools (basic Neanderthal type!) have to be specially made in order to drag out the mortar.

Obviously you can only clear a small area at a time, due to reach, so more bricks will need to be removed. Make sure when you do this that the holes are positioned so that you can clean both left and right within the cavity as far as you can reach. However, remember the stability of the wall is paramount. Only cut out two to three bricks long per section and leave at least four bricks before cutting the next section. It is advisable to only cut out four sections, if needed, on a wall before reinstatement. When the bricks are put back follow the rules previously explained concerning the type of bricks and mortar and leave the top bed joint out until set, then wedge with slate and point. In some instances an airbrick may be put in at intervals to allow more ventilation to the cavity to help stop future problems.

Another problem area for horizontal damp is at reveals due to splits or holes in the vertical DPC. In these cases, cut out the brickwork and replace the affected section of DPC, making sure to lap the DPC by a minimum of 100 mm top and bottom.

Safety tip

Gloves must be worn at all times as other materials could be under the initial surface such as nails, wood, even glass fragments. You must also take care around wall tie areas. It is very easy to catch your hand or part of your arm on a well placed tie

Vertical moisture

Vertical problems are normally due to a breakdown of the horizontal DPC, causing moisture to draw up through the ground into the brick or block work. If the external DPC is to be replaced, the brickwork is removed in sections in the same way as for cavity cleaning. If the whole wall is to be replaced, it is better to break the sections into four and name them sections A, B, C and D. Cut out all section As first. Lay the new DPC to the cut out opening, allowing for a minimum of 100 mm turn up at each end to allow lapping when those sections are replaced. Replace the brickwork but don't mortar the perp joints against the existing brickwork - wedge it as described previously. Then replace all section Bs, making sure the DPC is lapped with the previous section. Continue this for the remaining sections until the wall is completely replaced.

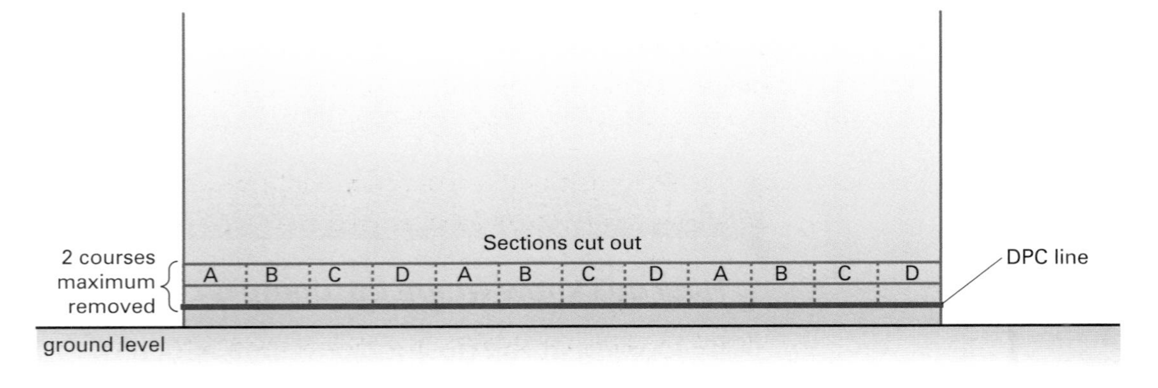

Figure 10.8 DPC sections

If the horizontal DPC has broken down on the internal wall, it is normally rectified by injecting a silicone-based liquid DPC.

The skirting boards and plaster are removed 1 m up from the floor. A series of holes are then drilled into the wall just above the existing DPC. The liquid is then pumped in and absorbed into the bricks. Once dry, the wall is re-plastered with a moisture resistant plaster. Sometimes liquid bitumen or sealer is painted onto the exposed brickwork prior to the plaster to stop any further problems. This work is normally carried out by a specialist company giving a minimum of a 10 year guarantee, but they may require the original plaster to be removed by the contractor.

If damp shows over a lintel, it could mean the cavity is bridged or no DPC tray has been fitted, most likely the latter. Cut out the brickwork in sections as before (probably not as many sections will be required) and clear if bridged, or fit a DPC cavity tray in sections, making allowance for lapping as previously described.

Also available is a plastic tray system, with each tray being two bricks long and having interlocking edges to connect to the next section. It has a flapped back edge which adjusts to meet the internal wall. This stops any moisture which is coming down the cavity from going behind the tray. Obviously with this system care must be taken with the measuring and placement of further trays, as the trays joining the sections may be too long or too short to fit into their correct position. The bricks are actually bedded into the tray, with plastic weep holes placed in the joint between the two bricks to allow any moisture to run back outside the building. This system is also used for stepped flashings where a pitch roof (for example, that of a garage) meets against the main building.

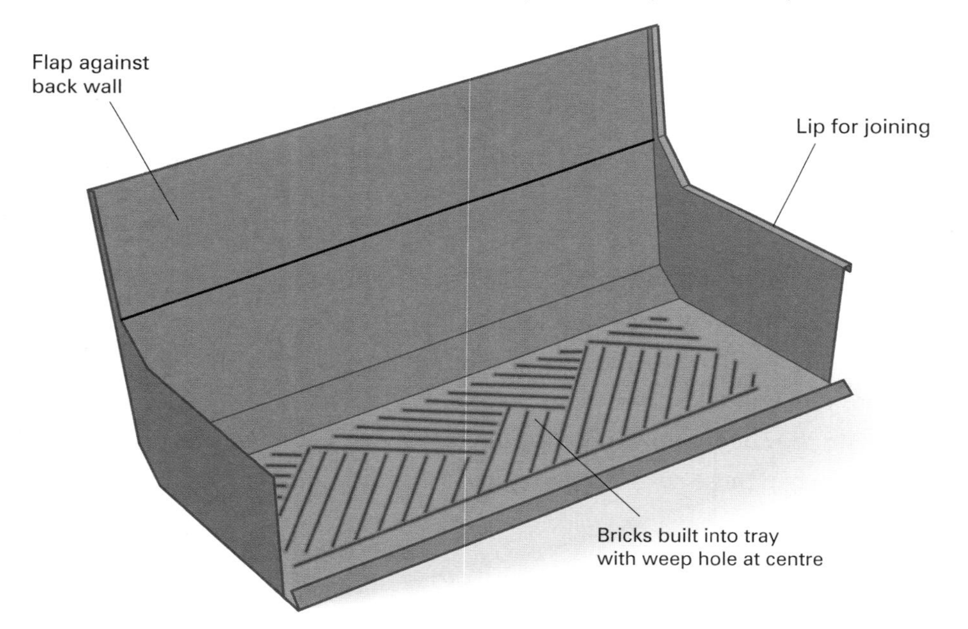

Figure 10.9 A cavity tray

FAQ

How do I know where the damp is coming in?

By looking at the position and area affected.

Damage to lintels or concrete cills

There are two main reasons for repairs to lintels or cills. One is edges breaking away and shear breaks. Lintels and cills are generally made of reinforced concrete. The front edge of a lintel or cill is the most exposed to the elements. Moisture absorbed into the concrete can freeze, causing expansion, or the reinforcement gets damp and rust forms on the steel, which also expands, causing the concrete to break away from the mass. The other reason for repairs to lintels and cills is cracking due to pressure from the weight above or movement around this area.

In the case of expansion the affected material could be removed, the exposed reinforcing coated with a rust treatment and rendered to finish, depending on the amount of damage. An alternative is to replace the lintel. If the lintel or cill is cracked or broken then this is the only option. The lintel will require dead shoring (as described on page 147) through the wall and the course of bricks above the lintel cut out. The lintel can then be carefully removed and replaced. A continuous DPC tray should be fitted on top of the lintel and the bricks reinstated and joint wedged and pointed. Weep holes should be positioned along the line of bricks to allow for any water drainage.

In the case of a cill replacement, care must be taken not to damage the frame. This time the bricks below the cill are removed, taking great care to ensure the cill does not suddenly drop trapping fingers or hands. A section should be cut out at each end under the cill, two courses in depth. Once removed, replace with dry bricks or timber blocks and wedge tight. Remove the rest of the two courses of brickwork below the cill. Slowly take out the wedges and allow the cill to sit on the blocks. Gradually remove the blocks end by end until the cill is clear of the frame. Take out the cill and dispose of correctly. The new cill should be fitted following the steps to remove the old cill in reverse order. Once in position build back the central brickwork and allow to dry - then wedge. Remove the end wedges and rebuild the remaining brickwork as before.

Note

In the case of a boot lintel, both internal and outer skins need to be removed

Remember

This operation should be carried out safely using the correct type of scaffolding to ensure all operatives are not put at risk

Material delivery

Most materials are delivered to site on lorries with crane off-loading equipment. This is a quick and efficient method of delivery as the materials can be positioned virtually anywhere they are required on site without having to be manhandled. If the materials are stored in specific areas (this is usual on larger sites), cranes are used to transport material around the site. If the correct procedures are followed there is little chance of injury to the workforce as no one has to touch the materials. The driver should be fully trained in the use of the equipment, so no other person should attempt to move materials in this way.

In some circumstances when materials are being delivered or moved on site, the driver may have problems seeing the position where the materials are to be placed. In these situations, a banksman is required to give hand signals to the driver to act as his or her eyes. The signals are normally for left, right, up, down and slow movement. The banksman should always stand in full view of the driver and the position the materials are to be moved to or connected by means of two way radio. He or she should be fully trained in this role and hold an up-to-date relevant certificate.

On the job: Mixing mortar

Mario has been asked to replace six broken bricks on an external wall to a property which is about 150 years old. His supervisor has left the materials in the garage. Mario has cut the bricks out as the joints were quite soft and is now ready to mix the mortar. On reaching the garage he finds the bricks, one bag of cement and one bag of sand. Is this OK?

Knowledge check

1. Name two ways to join brickwork on an extension to an existing property.
2. What are used to form edges ready for plastering?
3. Name three materials that can be used to support an opening.
4. Name two possible reasons for subsidence of a property.
5. What is the easiest way to check which way joists run?
6. What is the name of the person who gives signals to a driver unloading materials?
7. Why should you not over tighten props?
8. What is used to make sure joints are tight when replacing bricks?
9. Name two ways a property can gain extra space.
10. What are the two ways an opening can be finished ready for decoration?
11. What is the main cause of horizontal damp?
12. When toothing out, where is the best place to start from?
13. What is the temporary support system used for forming an opening called?
14. When cleaning out the cavity, how far below DPC should it be cleared?
15. Name two ways bricks can be matched.
16. What is the timber or steel called that goes through a wall as a temporary support

chapter 11

Study skills/Advanced examinations

OVERVIEW

There are two main purposes of an Advanced Construction Award (ACA): to develop your practical skills and theoretical knowledge of your chosen trade, and to help you work towards an NVQ and advanced modern apprenticeship full framework.

There are two different types of examination for the Advanced Construction Award: a practical-based skill test called the **phase test**, and a full written theory test. The revision and the practice for the phase test have already been fully covered in the previous chapters of this book, so this chapter will concentrate on:

- what the examination will be about
- what types of question will be asked
- how to break down a question to find out what is really being asked
- how examinations are marked
- what preparation is required
- sample examination.

What the examination will be about

The ACA examination originally consisted of two separate papers: one that was trade-specific, and one that was a core paper covering areas such as health and safety, which was sat by all trades. A carpenter would sit the core paper and the carpentry paper, and a bricklayer would sit the core paper and the bricklaying paper. Each paper took between two and three hours, and both were full written rather than multiple choice.

In 2006 the ACA examination changed from two test papers to one. The examination now has two parts: part A dealing with the core, and part B dealing with the trade specifics. The question papers have an average of 30 questions – 10 for core and 20 for trade – and a time limit of between two and three hours. To achieve a pass, the candidate must do well in both parts A and B. If, for example, a candidate scores 19 out of 20 on part B but only 2 out of 10 on part A, they will fail the examination.

The grading system for the examination is as follows:

- **fail** – the candidate has not shown sufficient knowledge and has not passed the examination. The candidate will have to re-sit the examination
- **pass** – the candidate has shown sufficient knowledge to pass the examination
- **credit** – the candidate has shown very good knowledge and achieved above the pass mark
- **distinction** – the candidate has shown outstanding knowledge and achieved well above the pass mark.

What types of question will be asked

Three different types of question will be asked during your ACA examination:

- short answer questions
- structured questions
- questions which refer you to a handout or separate sheet.

Short answer questions

Short answer questions contain one or more problems, which you are required to answer with one or two words, a single sentence, a small sketch or a simple calculation. The length of the answer may vary from question to question depending on the topic and the question being asked.

Typical examples of short answer questions, with answers

Q: State the meaning of the following abbreviations:

a) PUWER

b) COSHH

c) BSI

A: a) Provision and Use of Working Equipment Regulations

b) Control of Substances Hazardous to Health

c) British Standards Institute

Q: Describe briefly why it is important to have regular health and safety meetings.

A: To allow all staff and trades to find out what is happening and to have an input on the health and safety on the site.

Structured questions

Structured questions usually start with a statement containing some information, followed by a question or series of questions. The length of the answer required for each question will depend on what is being asked, as some of the questions may ask you to explain, state, list or even sketch your answer.

Typical examples of structured questions, with answers

Q: The Health and Safety (Safety Signs and Signals) Regulations apply to most work activities and premises.

a) Briefly explain within your own occupation where a safety sign would need to be displayed.

b) Sketch one safety sign and state what risk or hazard it is identifying.

A: a) A safety sign would need to be displayed in a building site environment on the outside of the site telling all who plan to enter what hazards there are and what actions must be taken.

b)

Safety sign

This safety sign is stating that there is a noise hazard and it is informing the viewer that they must wear ear protection.

Q: After climbing a ladder to reach the top of a scaffold you notice that a section of handrail is missing.

a) State what three actions must be done to prevent injury.

b) State who is responsible for checking the scaffold.

c) Explain briefly what should have been done.

A:

a) The three things that must be done are: 1) inform all those around you and those working on the scaffold to leave the scaffold; 2) position a sign or tape on the ladder to prevent anyone else accessing the scaffold; 3) inform the site agent and scaffolder.

b) The site agent is responsible. Even though he or she may delegate responsibility to a ganger or working foreman, the site agent is still responsible.

c) The scaffold should have been checked and, if it was found to be unsafe, then a red scaftag warning that the scaffold was unsafe should have been placed on the scaffold.

Remember

You must remember to write your name on the sheet and hand it in with your work or it will not get marked.

Questions that refer you to a handout or separate sheet

Some questions will refer you to a separate sheet contained within the question paper. This sheet will have a drawing or a table of sorts on it. The question will tell you what to do with the sheet, e.g. there may be a drawing of a site layout and the question will ask you to mark on the drawing a suitable place for a site office.

Typical example of a question that refers you to a separate sheet, with answers

Q: Complete the following accident report using an accident of your choice.

Report of an Accident, Dangerous Occurrence or Near Miss

Date of incident ______________ **Time of incident** ______________

Location of incident ______________________________

Details of person involved in accident

Name ______________________ Date of birth ______________

Address ______________________________

____

______________________ Occupation ______________________

Date off work (if applicable) __________ **Date returning to work** __________

Nature of injury ______________________________

Management of injury

☐ First Aid only ☐ Advised to see doctor

☐ Sent to casualty ☐ Admitted to hospital

Account of accident, dangerous occurrence or near miss
(Continued on separate sheet if necessary)

Witnesses to the incident
(Names, addresses and occupations)

Was the injured person wearing PPE? If yes, what PPE? ______________________

____

Signature of person completing form ______________________

Occupation ______________________ **Date** ______________

A:

Report of an Accident, Dangerous Occurrence or Near Miss

Date of incident 02/05/07 **Time of incident** 14:15

Location of incident On site

Details of person involved in accident

Name George Hill Date of birth 12/07/75

Address 123 Any Street, Hometown HT5 3AS

Occupation Carpenter

Date off work (if applicable) ______ **Date returning to work** ______

Nature of injury Head injury

Management of injury

- [ ] First Aid only
- [ ] Advised to see doctor
- [x] Sent to casualty
- [ ] Admitted to hospital

Account of accident, dangerous occurrence or near miss
(Continued on separate sheet if necessary)

Falling tiles from ceiling roof hit the victim badly on the back of the head, knocking him unconscious. An ambulance was called and first aid given.

Witnesses to the incident
(Names, addresses and occupations)

Peter Haining 56 House Lane
Site supervisor Hometown
HT1 5TQ

Was the injured person wearing PPE? If yes, what PPE?

Safety helmet, safety gloves

Signature of person completing form PHaining

Occupation Site supervisor **Date** 02/05/07

How to break down a question

Certain questions, like the ones above, are pretty straightforward and easy to understand, but with some questions it can be harder to work out just what is being asked.

> *Example*
>
> **Q: Briefly explain, within the realms of your own occupational area, the purpose and reasons for the need of each of the following within your workplace.**
>
> **a) safety policy**
>
> **b) method statements**
>
> **c) risk assessments.**

Here is how we can break down the question.

In the first part – **Briefly explain, within the realms of your own occupational area, the purpose and reasons for the need of each of the following within your workplace** – there are two parts of the question that you can disregard: '**within the realms of your own occupational area**' and '**within your workplace**'. These simply mean that the examination concerns your work.

If we remove the unnecessary parts of the question the question reads:

Briefly explain the purpose and reasons why you need each of the following:

a) safety policy
b) method statements
c) risk assessments.

We can then break the three parts into three separate questions:

Briefly explain the purpose and reasons why you need a safety policy.

Briefly explain the purpose and reasons why you need a method statement.

Briefly explain the purpose and reasons why you need a risk assessment.

So what we have done is taken a complex question and broken it down to make it easier to understand and answer.

Briefly explain, within the realms of your own occupational area, the purpose and reasons for the need of each of the following within your workplace:

a) safety policy
b) method statement
c) risk assessment.

A:

a) A safety policy states what that company will do to promote and maintain a safe and healthy workplace. The reason for it is to ensure the company employees work to the policy: meaning they work within health and safety law.

b) A method statement states what will be done on a job and in what order as well as stating what safety precautions must be taken. The reason for this is to ensure a proactive approach is taken where everything is planned.

c) Risk assessments are produced prior to a task starting and they take into account all hazards and put in place plans to reduce any risks. The reasons for a risk assessment are similar to a method statement meaning a company will take a proactive approach to health and safety.

Some single sentence questions you may encounter ask you more than one thing.

Example

Q: If you are heavily involved in conflict with other trades, how will this affect your work and how others treat you?

Some people will understand that the question is asking you two things, but others may only pick up on one of the parts of the question. The question is really asking you:

If you are heavily involved in conflict with other trades how will this affect how others treat you?

AND

If you are heavily involved in conflict with other trades how will this affect your work?

You can answer this type of question in two separate parts:

A: If you have conflict with other trades they may end up disliking you and treating you badly.

If you have conflict with other trades, then they may not help you, which could lead to you struggling to do your work.

Or you can combine the answers:

A: If you have conflict with other trades, they may end up disliking you; this could result in them not helping you, which could lead to you struggling to do your own work.

Either way of answering this question is fine as long as it is answered fully.

Throughout the examination the questions will ask you to sketch, state, list, define, describe, explain, etc. Each of these key words should help you identify what type of question is being asked and what type of answer should be given.

Questions or parts of questions that contain the words 'list', 'state' or 'name' usually require you to give a short answer consisting of one or two words or a single sentence.

Example

Q: State three items of PPE.

A: 1. gloves, 2. boots, 3. goggles

OR

Three items of PPE are boots, gloves and goggles.

Questions that ask you to define, describe or explain will require a longer answer.

Example

Q: Explain why we need PPE and when it should be used.

A: The reason we need PPE is to try and prevent accidents from occurring and PPE should be used when it is stated either by a sign or risk assessment. PPE should only be used as a last line of defence and should not be used as the sole way of preventing accidents.

Questions that contain the words 'sketch' or 'draw' will require you to provide drawings, remembering that a sketch need not be as detailed as a drawing. You must also look out for questions that contain two indicating words such as 'explain with the aid of sketches'.

How examinations are marked

The examination questions are set by a team of experienced people from industry and the awarding body. The examiners will have specific guidelines to follow when marking, and will have a selection of their marking sampled to ensure that they are not being too soft or too harsh.

Each question in the examination will have a specific maximum amount of marks.

Example

Q: Produce a safety checklist containing six items, for the erection of a step ladder. (6 marks)

This question is worth six marks, so the examiner will be looking for six things in your answer.

Examiners can only mark what is put in front of them, and can only give marks for correct or relevant information. They cannot deduct marks for wrong information, poor spelling or grammar, although the examiner must be able to read your answer.

Marks are awarded for each question on its own merits. Examiners must not let a poor or good answer to a previous question reflect on the marking of the next question, ensuring that each question gets the marks it deserves.

What preparation is required

Examination papers are set to check that you have the knowledge required to back up your practical ability – they are not set to trip you up or trick you. It is not the examiners' fault if you fail to understand or misread a question and give a wrong or incomplete answer.

There are two main reasons why people fail examinations:

- lack of knowledge or understanding
- failure to prepare.

Lack of knowledge or understanding

You should only enter or be entered for an examination if you feel that you have sufficient knowledge and understanding to pass. Even if you do have good knowledge, if you do not revise for the exam you will reduce your chances of passing. Revision is an extremely important part of study and unless facts and information are repeated, constantly used or revised they will soon be forgotten.

Revision should ideally start at the beginning of a course and not at the end, just because there is an exam coming up. How you do your revision is an individual thing and not all people will be able to revise in the same way, but some of these methods may help.

- Rewrite rough or scribbled notes neatly at the end of lessons.
- Try to pick out, underline or highlight key words in your notes or textbooks: remembering these key words can help to remember a whole topic.
- Read textbooks or technical brochures.
- Answer the *Knowledge Check* section at the back of each chapter in this book.
- Get a colleague to ask you questions and if you give an unsatisfactory answer, make a note of the question and revise that topic.
- Do the practice examinations at the end of this chapter.
- Use any technique you have found useful previously.

Failure to prepare

The saying goes 'if you fail to prepare, you must prepare to fail' and examinations are no exception. Preparation for the examination is of paramount importance and there are certain things you must do.

Prior to the exam:

- Ensure you have revised fully.
- Arrive at the examination centre in plenty of time: an hour early is better than ten minutes late.
- Ensure you have spare pencils, pens, etc.
- Check if you need to bring anything with you such as calculators, etc.
- Ensure you have had a good meal beforehand: hunger pains will not help your concentration.
- Make sure you have been to the toilet: trying to hold it in or asking to go to the toilet will disrupt your concentration.
- Get the contact details for the examination room in case any one needs you in an emergency.
- Switch off your mobile phone.

Once you are in the examination room:

- Listen carefully to any instructions.
- Read the instructions at the top of the paper.
- Read through the whole paper, underlining any key words or points that may help you to answer that question later.
- Try to answer the questions you find easiest first as this will allow you to gain confidence and get some answers done (as opposed to sitting looking at a difficult question for an hour).
- Do *not* miss out or leave any question blank. If you are running short of time try to put something down that will at least get you some marks.
- If you have time at the end, re-read the questions and your answers to see if there is anything else you can add.
- Use the full time of the examination if needed. People have failed simply because they thought they had finished and left as soon as they could without checking their work.
- If you have to use additional sheets, ensure that your name and details are on them and that they are handed in with your work.
- Ensure that you have answered the question fully. If the question is worth three marks, make sure you have three marks' worth written down.
- If a question asks for five things and you can think of six then put six down, as one of the six you are thinking of may be wrong.
- Make sure your writing and sketches are legible: if you are struggling to read it, so will the examiners.

Once you have finished:

- Double and triple check your answers.
- Follow the procedure stated before the exam started to get an examiner's attention.
- If others are still working, leave the room and building quietly.

If you have revised and prepared well, then you will stand a good chance of passing.

Sample examination

When you are ready, try the following practice examination paper. It is best to practise using examination conditions, so try to ensure that you give yourself time to do the exam in one sitting.

Practice paper

You will need the following for this examination:

- answer book or blank paper with which to write your answers
- drawing instruments
- blue/black pen
- non-programmable calculator.

This exam will consist of two sections:

- Section 1: ten questions relating to core knowledge
- Section 2: twenty questions relating to the trade.

Candidates must achieve at least a pass mark on each section. The maximum marks for each question are shown in brackets.

Section 1 – Answer all **ten** questions. All questions carry equal marks.

1 Before commencing any work within an operational area, describe **four** important considerations. (4 marks)

2 State **four** reasons why the correct storage of materials is important. (4 marks)

3 With the aid of sketches, explain how on a mobile tower scaffolding the

a) base wheels can be prevented from turning (2 marks)

b) tower's stability can be increased allowing it to be built higher. (2 marks)

4 Describe briefly how the internal working environment can be improved during the construction of new buildings during the cold winter months. (4 marks)

5 Describe **four** features of a good transport route into and within a construction site. (4 marks)

6 State **four** responsibilities of an employer under the Health and Safety at Work Act. (4 marks)

7 State **two** important factors for

a) holding regular safety meetings (2 marks)

b) holding regular progress meetings. (2 marks)

8 State what initial actions are to be taken when there is a suspected theft on site. (4 marks)

9 List **one** construction material that you are familiar with, which may cause problems for an operative when manual handling and state what precautions should be taken. (4 marks)

10 Describe **two** planning strategies used in your occupational area for preventing disruption of work due to

a) non-delivery of materials (2 marks)

b) conflicting trade interests. (2 marks)

Section 2 – Answer all **eighteen** questions

1 a) Show by way of a sketch an external plinth return brick. (2 marks)

b) Explain what the function of this brick is. (2 marks)

2 State what the most suitable material is for

a) ensuring minimal heat loss in the inner leaf of a cavity wall (2 marks)

b) acting as a horizontal damp proof course to a boundary wall. (2 marks)

3 An area is to be filled with hardcore in readiness to receive the over-site concrete. The area is 6.70 m long and 5.50 m wide. There is an average depth of 0.20 m. Calculate:

a) the quantity of hardcore required given that the density = 2.000 kg / m^3 (2 marks)

b) the total cost of the hardcore given that the price per tonne = £18.00. (2 marks)

4 Briefly explain what effect the following additives would have on a mortar mix

a) retarders (2 marks)

b) accelerators (2 marks)

5 Efflorescence is a white powder type substance which appears on the face of brickwork

a) Explain what causes efflorescence. (2 marks)

b) Explain how can efflorescence be removed. (2 marks)

6 a) Identify TWO optical instruments that can be used to set out a building with right angled corners. (2 marks)

b) Calculate the length of the diagonals on the drawing shown below.

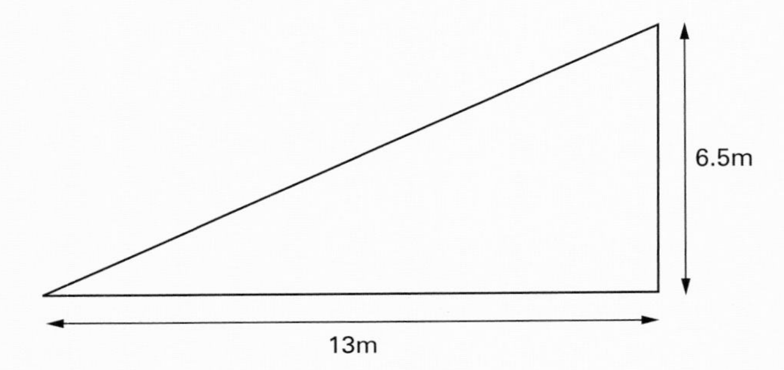

(2 marks)

7 State FOUR regulations that must be complied with when using a portable masonry saw on site. (4 marks)

8 With the aid of a sketch show what a pistol brick looks like and briefly explain where one would be used. (4 marks)

9 Sketch and name two methods that are used to fix timber frames as the work proceeds. (4 marks)

10 a) Name the inclined surface from which an arch is sprung.

b) Name the external or outer curve of the arch.

c) Name the bricks used for building an arch.

d) Name the brickwork that supports the arch on either side. (4 marks)

11 State FOUR positions on a dwelling where a DPC may be needed. (4 marks)

12 Calculate the amount of standard size bricks (215 × 102.5 × 65 mm) that are required to construct the 1 brick wall shown below allowing 10% waste.

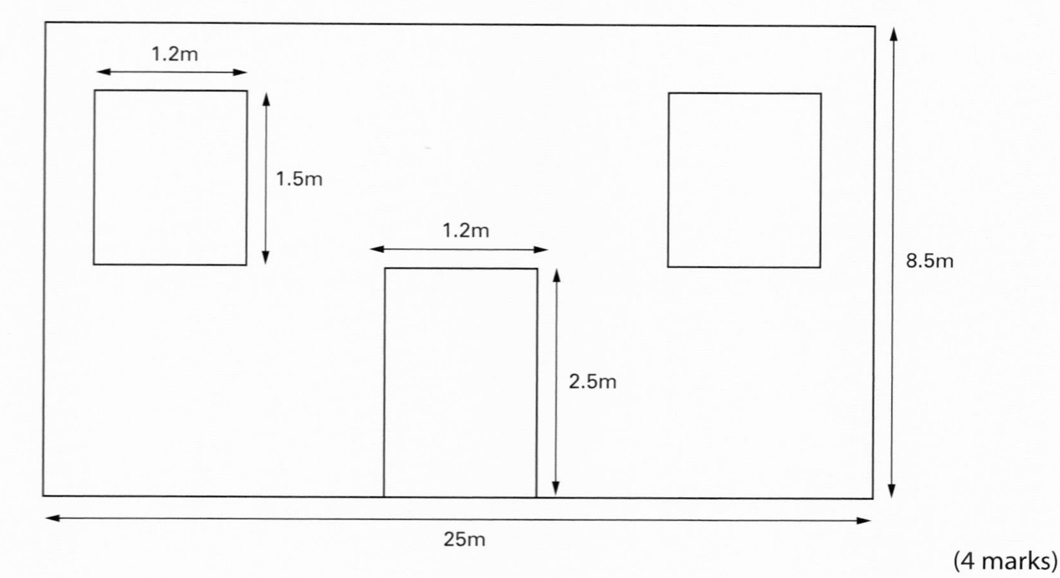

(4 marks)

13 State FOUR items of information that would be placed on a storey rod. (4 marks)

14 List the correct sequence of operations to set out the voussoirs template to an axed semi-circle arch. (4 marks)

15 State the number of striking points required for both of the following arches

a) two ringed semi-circular arch (2 marks)

b) segmental arch. (2 marks)

16 State FOUR checks that a bricklayer would make on an existing opening that is to receive a decorative panel. (4 marks)

17 Name four different types of special plinth bricks. (4 marks)

18 Sketch a cross section view of the following joints

a) flush

b) struck and cut

c) half round

d) weather struck. (4 marks)

NVQ Level 3 Trowel Occupations

Chapters	Unit VR 01 Conform to General Workplace Safety	Unit VR 209 Confirm Work Activities and Resources for the Work	Unit VR 210 Develop and Maintain Good Working Relationships	Unit VR 211 Confirm the Occupational method of Work	Unit VR 42 Erect Masonry Cladding	Unit VR 44 Erect Thin Joint Masonry Structures	Unit VR 48 Set Out Complex Masonry Structures	Unit VR 49 Erect Complex Masonry Structures	Unit VR 50 Repair and Maintain Masonry Structures
Health and safety	Pages 1 to 16			Pages 1 to 16	Pages 1 to 16	Pages 1 to 16	Pages 1 to 16	Pages 1 to 16	Pages 1 to 16
Building		Pages 17 to 38		Pages 17 to 38					
Planning and Work Programmes		Pages 41 to 54	Pages 41 to 54	Pages 41 to 54					
The Building Process		Pages 55 to 67		Pages 55 to 67					
Thin Joint Masonry Construction						Pages 69 to 80			
Complex Masonry Structures							Pages 81 to 99	Pages 81 to 99	
Fire places and Flues								Pages 105 to 118	
Erect Masonry Cladding					Pages 119 to 130				
Decorative Panels								Pages 131 to 139	
Repair and Maintain masonry Structures									Pages 141 to 159
Study Skills									

Advanced Construction Award – Trowel Occupations						
	Unit ACA 173 Assist in Establishing the Operational Area	Unit ACA 174 Assist with Progressing Operations	Unit ACA 175 Assist with Organising Resources	Unit ACA 176 Co-ordinate Self and Others to Erect Complex brick and Block Work	Unit ACA 177 Co-ordinate Self and Others to Produce Complex Walling Details	Unit ACA 178 Co-ordinate and Produce Complex Construction Aids
Chapters						
Health and safety	Pages 1 to 16			Pages 1 to 16	Pages 1 to 16	Pages 1 to 16
Building Documentation	Pages 17 to 29	Pages 17 to 38	Pages 17 to 38			
Planning and Work Programmes	Pages 41 to 54		Pages 41 to 54			
The Building Process	Pages 55 to 68		Page 55			
Thin Joint Masonry Construction	Not Applicable					
Complex Masonry Structures				Pages 100 to 103	Pages 81 to 99	Pages 81 to 99
Fire Places & Flues					Pages 105 to 118	
Erect Masonry Cladding	Not Applicable					
Decorative Panels					Pages 131 to 139	
Repairing and Maintaining Masonry Structures	Not Applicable					
Study Skills	Not Applicable					

access entrance, a way in

acute angle this is an angle less than 90°

aesthetic the 'principles of beauty, taste and art'

aircrete a product name for blocks manufactured from autoclaved aerated concrete

amenities facilities such as toilets, rest areas, etc.

asbestosis a serious lung condition caused by breathing in asbestos

blown plaster or render no longer adhering to the interior brick or block wall

brick slips these usually have the same dimensions in relation to length and height as the standard clay bricks used in traditional construction methods. However, the thickness of the slip is normally no more than 25 mm. Generally brick slips are made from exactly the same material as the standard clay bricks

building regulations a set of regulations brought in to deal with poor housing conditions, which now restrict what can be built, how and where

compressive forces these relate to the weight imposed from above

concave means rounded inwards

contamination when harmful chemicals or substances pollute something (e.g.water)

convex means curved outwards

cured the mortar has set and reached its full strength

decibel (dB) the standard unit for measuring noise level

dermatitis a skin condition where the affected area is red, itchy and sore

discrepancies when there is a difference or variation between two things that should be the same

dismantle take apart, take down carefully

duration how long something goes on

egress exit, a way out

electrocution death through coming into contact with an electric current

elevation refers to a vertical face of a building

employer the person or company someone works for

employee the person employed by the employer, the member of staff

hazardous dangerous or unsafe

health and Safety Executive (HSE) the legislation laws or the making of laws

impregnated soaked right through

inconsistencies when things are not the same, not consistent

interim in the time between, for the time being, as a holding measure

lateral belonging to, relating to, located at or affecting the side

legislation laws or the making of laws

load-bearing walls referred to as load-bearing support the load from roofs and floors

making a risk assessment measuring the dangers of an activity against the likelihood of accidents taking place

objectives aims, purposes

obligation something you have a duty or a responsibility to do

obtuse angle this is an angle greater than 90°

omission something that has not been done or has been missed out

open fire form of heating contained within a fireplace recess

outbuilding a shed or storage area connected to the main building

penalty clause a clause in a contract saying a fine has to be paid, or some other penalty made, if a certain thing happens, e.g. the job overruns

people days a way of expressing how long it will take to do something by looking at how many people will be needed for how long

phase test a practical-based skills test

pinch rod a piece of timber cut to the size of the opening and used to measure the distance between the reveals at various stages during their construction

PPE personal protective equipment, such as gloves, a safety harness or goggles

pre-fabricated refers to cladding components which are pre-made and designed to minimise the amount of installation work required

proactive acting in advance, before something happens (e.g. an accident)

prohibition a ban, saying something cannot happen or be done

prosecute take someone to court for committing a crime

prospective likely or possible in the future, but not actually happening or approved now

quoin the corner of a wall

RCD residual current device, a device that will shut the power down on a piece of electrical equipment if it detects a change in the current, thus preventing electrocution

reactive acting after something happens, in response to it

regularised joists joists run through a saw to ensure that they are all the same depth

remit scope, job, the areas an organisation or individual has to cover

residential where people live, rather than a business district, for example

retention where the client holds a small percentage of the full payment back for a specified period in case of defects being discovered.

safety policy document outlining the company's commitment and stating what they plan to do to ensure that all work is carried out as safely as possible

superstructure work above DPC

solvent a substance that dissolves another e.g. paint stripper

stipulation a condition of an agreement, a particular term of a contract

surveillance carefully watching over or keeping an eye on

sustainability the ability to last or carry on, how easy something is to keep going

swimming effect this is where the blocks which have been laid, float on the wet mortar bed as the weight upon them increases. This dramatically affects the setting time of the block work structure and restricts the height to which blocks can be laid in any one day

tipping this is where, if care is not taken during the laying process, the whole corbel may tip forward and quite possibly topple over

toothing cutting out existing brickwork to join new

traversing means to go over or trace over the face of the arch with the template to ensure the correct shape has been achieved when producing the template

'U' values these indicate the thermal performance of a material in different situations

vial a small glass bottle containing the bubble used to give a reading when plumbing or levelling brick or block work

vibration white finger condition that can be caused by using vibrating machinery (usually for very long periods of time). The blood supply to the fingers is reduced which causes pain, tingling and sometimes spasms (shaking) should be the same